NEGATIVE GRAVITY

A Life of Beatrice Shilling

———•—•——•——

Matthew Freudenberg

Dedicated to all those who worked long, uncomfortable and often
dangerous hours at the Royal Aircraft Establishment
during the second world war.

Published in 2003 by Charlton Publications
Orchard House, Creech St Michael, Taunton TA3 5PF

Publications

The Isle of Man TT — An illustrated history
Aston Publications 1990

ISBN   0-9546165-0-2

Printed in England by Acanthus Press Ltd, Wellington, Somerset

Contents

Acknowledgments

This book could not have been written without the help and encouragement of Anne and Dennis Lock, Beatrice Shilling's sister and brother-in-law. Their memories and Beatrice's correspondence with her husband George Naylor while he served in the RAF during the war are the foundations of this book. I am grateful to David Woodford, Beatrice's nephew, for allowing me to make use of these letters and for his own recollections of his aunt. More family and pre-RAE background were provided by Elizabeth "Biddy" Fraser-Davies, Dorothy King, Janet Ray, Sheila Anscombe (nee McGuffie), and Dr. T. E. Broadbent of Manchester University.

My special thanks to Bob Newton for his account of working with Beatrice at Farnborough during the war and for his firm guidance in aircraft matters. Among other colleagues at the Royal Aircraft Establishment Tom Bowling, Peter Harben, Bernard Harding, Roy Hawkins, Dave Hull and Brenda Rimmer have been particularly helpful. For insights into the life of a bomber pilot I am indebted to Clem Koder, DSO, a senior to George in his Lancaster unit, 625 Squadron.

Rolls-Royce Heritage Trust has been generous in providing information and photographs of the Merlin and various Bristol engines. The Trust's Historical Series include outstanding accounts of the design, development and wartime service of the Merlin engine. The Women's Engineering Society, particularly Cathy MacGillivray, uncovered much evidence of the importance of this organisation to Beatrice's career as an engineer. I thank DERA, the successor to the Royal Aircraft Establishment, for permission to reproduce photographs from the Farnborough Records Department, and Dick Snell and Elizabeth Grimshaw for their help in finding relevant material. The present main occupant of the Farnborough site, QinetiQ, continues to help the work of the Farnborough Air Sciences Trust of preserving and displaying the site's history.

Mike Budd, together with Chris Wiblin and Tony Wood of the Rapier Register, provided information and photographs from the postwar motor racing years of Beatrice and George.

Brian Kervell, colleague and friend of Beatrice Shilling and later curator and archivist of the RAE Museum not only supplied much detail about the functioning of the Royal Aircraft Establishment but offered to read and correct the manuscript of this book, an offer I accepted gratefully. Finally, thanks to my wife Wendy for her patient support and constructive criticism in spite of my many hours away from home in pursuit of "the other woman."

I have not corrected the grammar or spelling of any correspondence quoted. Although I have strong engineering interests I am not a mechanical engineer. Any errors of fact or technology are my own.

Introduction

Beatrice Shilling became an engineer in 1929, a trespasser, at that time, in male territory, having decided in her teens that this was her vocation. Her main achievements were technical and mostly to do with aircraft, so the story of her life would be incomplete without some detail of her work as an engineer at the Royal Aircraft Establishment at Farnborough. But there was much more to Beatrice Shilling than a gift for solving technical problems. She had a dry sense of humour and total impatience with ceremony that did not always please her superiors. She was an outstanding motorcycle racer but nearly killed herself racing cars. Her marriage was not a tranquil one, but it was strengthened by enforced separation while her husband was a pilot in Bomber Command; their regular correspondence took them through the many difficulties of those three years.

During the second World War Beatrice Shilling became widely known, at least by the RAF, for solving a problem that affected fighter aircraft in action before and during the Battle of Britain. This problem was a tendency of the Rolls-Royce engine that powered Spitfires and Hurricanes to hesitate or cut out completely just as the pilot entered a dive in pursuit of, or in flight from, an enemy aircraft, a dangerous handicap not shared by the opposing Messerschmitts. The cause was not easy to find, but Beatrice found it by tests and calculation, solving it with a very simple device which became known as "Miss Shilling's Orifice".

Although she was ambitious, she did not work at making influential friends and criticised her superiors at the Royal Aircraft Establishment if she did not respect their efforts. In spite of this she reached a senior position in the Establishment and received the OBE for her work during the war.

One

Childhood and Schooldays

After a short pioneer flight in 1908, Samuel Franklin Cody's "British Army Aeroplane No. 1" became the first aircraft to fly a distance in excess of a mile in Britain, taking off from Laffan's Plain near the Army Balloon Factory close to Farnborough, where it had been built on May 14th 1909. In May of that year of great activity in early aviation, Beatrice Shilling was an infant just two months old and she may have heard the droning Antoinette engine of Cody's machine through the window of the family home. The flight was watched by the Prince of Wales, later King George V, and Cody continued to develop powered aircraft in Hampshire until his death in a flying accident in 1913.

Beatrice was born on March 8th 1909, to Henry and Annie Shilling in Waterlooville, Hampshire. Henry, in his fifties when he married Annie, had been a farmer and later a master butcher. He now owned properties in Surbiton and Guildford that brought the family a comfortable income. There were two other daughters, Nora and Anne, aged three and four. Mrs Shilling, known throughout her life both to her family and officially as Nancy, was born a Dulake; one of her relatives had traced descent from Sir Lancelot du Lac with the help of the Royal College of Heralds, but Nancy regarded this as an amusing rather than an elevating connection.

Beatrice was born an Edwardian, and much of the Edwardian way of life flowed on until the First World War was under way in 1914. Most people believed in the security and rightness of a far-flung Empire. The theatre, art and music hall thrived and were widely enjoyed; a comfortable and sociable life was made possible by servants for most middle and upper-class families. It was a rare Francophile era, for Edward VII's enthusiasm and good humour had created an "Entente Cordiale" with France. Men were proud to be British.

Women, and the working populations of industrial cities, the coal-mining regions of Wales and the north, though also proud to be British, had less to celebrate. Poor working conditions and low wages were the background to the rapid and aggressive growth of trade unions, which were confronted by employers who believed that Lloyd George was introducing socialism with his plans for health and unemployment benefits. 1911 was a year of strikes and lockouts, leading to violence and street fighting, with troops helping the police to try to control riots in Liverpool and South Wales, where several rioters were shot dead.

The professions of law, engineering and politics were all but closed to women, and girls were expected to become nurses, but not doctors. Land and property were usually handed down to male descendants, often obliging unmarried daughters to seek unskilled and low-paid work. There were a few women of exceptional determination who had won recognition as leaders in a field of science: Marie Curie who with her husband discovered radium; Lillian Gilbreth, a pioneer in industrial engineering (also known as work study); Hertha Ayrton, the first woman to be elected to membership of the Institute of Electrical Engineers on the basis of her original work on the nature of electric arcs.

Women did not have the right to vote. During 1909 the campaign for votes for women was particularly violent. In public demonstrations suffragettes, members of the Women's Social and Political Union, deliberately broke the law in the hope that the prison sentences and harsh treatment that many of them received would open people's eyes to the injustice of denying women the vote. Suffragettes harassed politicians vigorously, going so far as to blow up part of Lloyd George's house, a tactic which won more influential enemies than friends. But it was not a burning issue to men like Asquith or Winston Churchill, and they succeeded in shelving votes for women until 1917, when women over the age of 30 were finally enfranchised.

Well distanced in rural Hampshire from flying bricks, the Shilling family welcomed the arrival of little Beatrice. To Nora and Anne Beatrice was "Baby", and Baby was what she was called until she started school. They played well together, though Beatrice was not a tranquil child. Baby threw impressive tantrums, which alarmed her mother because they could result in convulsions. She also bit, and Anne remembers the conversation when Nancy tried to stop this:

Mother: *"Baby, you mustn't bite your sister."*
Beatrice: *"Have."*
Mother: *"Well, say that you're sorry."*
Beatrice: *"Shan't."*

A trivial incident, but unrepentant brevity remained her style throughout her life.

In 1914 the family moved to Surbiton, Surrey, where Henry Shilling owned the freeholds of four shops, one of them the only butcher's shop at that time. All three girls went to Surbiton High School for Girls. Baby, at five years, joined the kindergarten, and depending on the weather, the girls walked or took a tram. One cannot call a schoolgirl "Baby", and

Beatrice, her schoolwork all carefully identified with "B. Shilling", chose to be called simply "B".

Nora, Anne and Beatrice were good scholars and received certificates for their drawing and needlework at regular intervals. One's suspicion that Beatrice's cool view of authority led to occasional confrontations is confirmed by a letter she wrote in 1944 to her husband, who was training to become a bomber pilot and resented being "ticked off."

"I don't think you were naughty enough at school – I was ticked off many times a day at school. I used to look so miserable that they used to apologise for talking so harshly. If you could establish that if you got ticked off you burst into tears you could get away with anything."

It is unlikely that George ever tried this in the RAF.

The girls were also good at sports, and the two younger sisters played energetic games together at home. On one occasion while climbing around a room in the absence of their mother, Beatrice fell out of a window onto the concrete below. Anne rushed out in fear for her sister, wondering how she would give their mother bad news, to find Beatrice picking herself up. "S'all right" she said, "fell on my head."

In 1920 the family moved to Dorking; the girls now went to Dorking High School. All three gained more certificates of merit in needlework, but while Nora enjoyed it and produced beautiful work, Anne and Beatrice had no time for it. Both preferred to use tools at home to make things out of wood, and Beatrice became so proficient with her Meccano construction kits that at twelve she entered, and won, a prize in a national competition set by *Meccano Magazine*. Her entry was a working model of a spinning wheel, inspired by seeing one in use at an exhibition that she visited with her mother. However, her sights were set on something more exciting. In 1949, in an interview for an article in *John Bull* magazine, she related that she used to go on cycle rides with Nora and Anne, but she became so annoyed with being left behind by her sisters with their longer, stronger legs that at ten she started to save up for a motorcycle. At fourteen she had enough for a basic machine – bought it and trundled it home.

Her sister Anne remembers sharing in this purchase – "a little tiny motorbike which she asked me to go shares with". It was a two-stroke Royal Enfield. Both girls used to ride it and Beatrice would take Anne on the pillion. Beatrice, who at fourteen had complete confidence in her ability to assemble any machine that she had taken to bits, regularly took the Royal Enfield's engine apart. She also stripped and reassembled her father's rifles.

Henry Shilling was a first class shot with a rifle. As a young man he joined the Twelfth Surrey Rifle Volunteer Battalion, one of many such battalions active in the second half of the nineteenth century, which trained with marches, annual camps and above all, rifle shooting competitions, to help defend the country should the need arise. Henry shot for his Battalion in the annual Queen's Prize competition at Bisley, and the clock that he won as first prize in his Battalion's annual shoot in 1877 was still telling the time on Beatrice's mantlepiece a hundred years later. His enthusiasm for target shooting never left him, and Beatrice was taught how to handle a gun. She wrote an article for Guns Review in 1978, in which she described her introduction to rifles.

"At the outbreak of the Great War, the Army asked for Service-type rifles and my father handed in several. However, in case of invasion, he kept two and a good supply of ammunition – he was a reservist and mother had shown some promise with a Lee-Metford. His rifles and ammunition were never locked up, but safety rules on handling were strictly enforced – which made the rifles rather unrealistic "props" for "Cowboys and Indians" and other War games! Being interested I learned how a rifle worked, how to clean it, and how important cleaning was. When I was older I was taught to fire a 303 and this was done quite informally, firing into the chalk of the Surrey hills. The advice I remember was, "Take each shot separately. Don't hurry – the last shot is as important as the first. Always fire experimental rounds remotely and not in a gun you value."

This suggests that some bullets were home-made, an activity that would have appealed to Beatrice.

Her ease and pleasure in understanding, stripping down and rebuilding anything mechanical strengthened in Beatrice with ownership of a motorcycle. She did well in maths and science at school, and some time in her fifteenth year she decided that she would become an engineer.

For a woman in the 1920s a career in lion-taming would have been more realistic. Opposition to women as engineers was deeply rooted in industry, the trades unions and the professional associations such as the Institution of Mechanical Engineering. "The average woman does not possess the same engineering instinct as the average man" was the opinion expressed by the manager of the Education Research Department of the British Westinghouse Company to the Daily News. This opinion was also voiced by men whose real fear was competition from women for jobs at a time when the unemployed never numbered less than one million.

Beatrice's parents did not oppose her wishes, although her father thought little of them. Her mother understood that not only was she was determined, but that if her gift for mechanics was not encouraged, she would become greatly frustrated. Anne had chosen to become a dancer, and trained in classical ballet. As Beatrice had passed her seventeenth birthday, she would leave school the same summer after matriculating, yet opportunities for training in engineering seemed non-existent.

Dorking High School did not, understandably, include engineering among the occupations towards which it guided its school-leavers, but it was here that a glimmer of hope appeared to Mrs Shilling. The school received a circular letter from the "Association of Head Mistresses in Public Secondary Schools, in Association with the Ministry of Labour, Department of Employment and Insurance", setting out a scheme devised by two leading members of the Women's Engineering Society.

This Society had been founded in 1919, primarily to protect the right to work of women who had been employed during the Great War in engineering trades, mainly in arms manufacture, and many of whom, particularly war widows, wanted to continue in these trades. It developed to encourage the participation of women in training and in the practice of engineering, a role which it continues to play strongly today. In the early twenties the WES suffered a conflict of interests between those who wanted a strictly professional association, and those who were concerned to give women much broader opportunities for work and education at all levels of engineering.

Those who stood for support of women at all levels of engineering won the day, against bitter opposition from founder members, whose industrial and social connections, as well as their hard work, had helped to create the Society. Two of the strongest fighters for the new constitution of the Society were behind the letter that was sent in May 1926 to secondary girls' schools throughout the country, including Dorking High School. They were Margaret Partridge BSc, a lively and enterprising electrical engineer who ran a company based in Exeter, and Caroline Haslett, Secretary of the

Women's Engineering Society.

The letter read:

"An exceptionally interesting vacancy has been notified to the committee. Miss Partridge BSc, director of the Exe Valley Electricity Co., and other Electrical undertakings in Devonshire is at present engaged in a contract for the generation and installation of electricity at Bungay, Suffolk, and requires a pupil to learn the work at Bungay. The training will aim at making the selected girl proficient to assist in taking charge of the plant and electrical development of the district."

The letter went on to say that a knowledge of mathematics and physics and "a definite inclination" towards practical work were required. Headmistresses were asked to pass on the names of girls interested in the post. Mrs Shilling persuaded Beatrice to reply to the letter.

The background to the recruitment circular was this: in the mid 1920s County Councils were inviting tenders for installing electricity in country areas, backed by the Electricity (Supply) Act which encouraged private enterprises, and Margaret Partridge and her partners seized the opportunity with both hands. On January 10th 1926 she wrote to Caroline Haslett:

"We are to open up Power Stations all over the West at the rate of three or four a year and your share of the job is to supply students who in two years or three become full blown station engineers running all these power stations, and each training the next student for the next station that is to be opened."

Margaret Partridge was partnered by Dr John Purves in the drive to electrify rural Devon, and their success in winning contracts rapidly outstripped their recruitment of personnel. She was impatient to get results from the letter to schools and on June 30th 1926 wrote to her friend Caroline Haslett:

"Re this damsel – do you really think there is any likelihood of a girl presenting herself who wants to learn engineering? . . . If I had ever thought that it would take so long I wouldn't have troubled about the engineering side – but just taken on a typist and started with a boy or young man for the engineering side."

Perhaps she had not allowed for the timing of school terms and exams for matriculation. Whatever the reason, Beatrice or her mother communicated with Margaret Partridge toward the end of the summer term at Dorking High School in July, 1926. Although she was only seventeen, and the circular letter had required candidates to be not less than eighteen years of age, Beatrice was offered the job. She had become an apprentice electrical engineer.

Beatrice's mother, Nancy, about 1900. *Anne and Dennis Lock*

Nancy Shilling and her daughters, Beatrice sitting on her lap. *David Woodford*

Beatrice aged about four. *Anne and Dennis Lock*

After his pioneering flight on October 16, 1908 ended in a crash, Samuel Frank Cody demonstrates his skill with the lasso to get a rope round the Cody 1 Aeroplane. He flew over a mile shortly after Beatrice was born.

Science and Society Picture Library, Science Museum London.

Two

Apprentice Engineer

Beatrice left Dorking after the end of the summer term for Bampton, a small town about twenty-five miles north of Exeter, and a few miles south of Exmoor. Margaret Partridge had arranged accommodation and started her programme of training straight away. She wrote to Caroline Haslett.

"I have managed to give Beatrice Shilling over a week's wiring work, and it seems to be turning out a great success. I really think she is a great acquisition to the firm – able to enjoy any new experience – and not in the least superior or blase – the fault of the very young at times. She has a wicked joy in making all the YWCA hostel stand their hair on end by tales of her unladylike exploits when wiring."

Margaret Partridge was obviously pleased at the way Beatrice tackled her new life in Devon. Her plan was to teach Beatrice the basics of internal house wiring, then connection to the external supply, then to give her lots of practice in connecting houses in Bampton to the electricity generating plant that the South West Electricity Company had installed in the town. Generation was normally by diesel engines installed in whatever buildings she could get hold of at a low price. She was the managing partner, responsible for making the business work, and personally organised sales, legal agreements, staff, installation work and dealt with contractors, disputes, unpaid bills and other miscellaneous problems. She did this not only in Bampton but in three other locations where she and the technical director, Dr John Purves had won contracts. The Company was also looking for more locations to introduce to electricity.

Fortunately she had a large capacity for work and for enjoying the oddities of human behaviour. At Bungay in Essex she hit on a way to waken the enthusiasm of the timid young staff whom she was teaching electrical engineering.

"Almost the entire staff come from seaside places, and consequently swim like fishes. So in order to retain their self-respect and to prove that although I may know far more about electricity than they do, I still have something to learn, they have arranged to teach me to swim. The process is I fall into a 40 foot deep pool – swim a few strokes and promptly proceed to drown. Then everyone else proceeds to pull me out again . . .When the body is tired of drowning . . . we start with many pencils and paper to study A. C. induction motors, three phase and single phase and what not."

Beatrice also learned from Margaret Partridge, and from Miss Rowbotham, who had practical engineering experience with the Swanson Pump Company, and was particularly helpful in teaching Beatrice advanced mathematics. Miss Rowbotham joined the South West Electricity Company as a partner in 1927, working from South Molton where Beatrice, though still working as an outdoor linesman and indoor wiring installer, had advanced to learning to design and lay out generating plant.

"Beatrice Shilling is going to do very well indeed. She has taken over a big power station plan to do – plan and projection – and set it all out and traced it with a real engineer's understanding. Not traced only but carried out layout, and all. Also the

boys – those who have seen her – like her. They couldn't stand Miss Shattner and softly and silently managed to get rid of her while I was away in Leeds."

So reported Margaret Partridge to Caroline Haslett.

When Beatrice took holidays at home, her mother was happy to hear about her success in Devon and interested to learn about the women engineering graduates who were helping to advance her training. Mr Shilling was still sceptical about the point of it all, but when he happened to complain that he had to get out of bed to turn off his bedroom light, Beatrice wired up his bedside light so that it could be switched on and off at the door and from his bed. It seems that this did impress him enough for him to agree that she was learning something useful.

It was a tough apprenticeship for a teenage girl fresh from school. Once Beatrice had learned the skills of electrician and linesman, Miss Partridge was not always there to deal with the problems that the citizens of Bampton and South Molton put in her way. Demands for last minute changes in the wiring plan were everyday matters, but disputes over the height, direction and safety of power cables could be violent enough to need the intervention of a policeman. There was also accidental damage to customers' walls or ceilings when wiring was put through them; on at least one occasion, Beatrice told her sisters, she went through the ceiling with the wiring. She was able to restore householders' confidence, and probably took a pride in dealing with setbacks without calling for help from one of the partners of the South West Electricity Company.

Other girls beside Beatrice joined Margaret Partridge's company as trainees (Beatrice was the second), some with more success than others. In her correspondence with Caroline Haslett,

Margaret Partridge complains of a girl who is too nervous to enter the generating room on her own, and another who is just "hopeless". Marjorie Bell, President of the Women's Engineering Society, 1957-1958, wrote in her memoirs of joining the company as a trainee and working at the Bungay power station:

"Doing everything but mostly shovelling coal into the retorts. I read the meters, prepared the bills, ran the office and looked after the showroom. I learnt nothing."

Although she relished practical work and worked well with people, it cannot have been all fun for Beatrice in Devon. She lived in the local YWCA or in "digs", a long way from home, earning a trainee's wage of twenty-five shillings a week. She would not make friends of people she did not respect, and to be "one of the girls" would have been out of the question. She must have wondered at times where her training was going to lead. She had joined the company shortly after the General Strike ended in 1926, the strikers having failed to alter the government's belief that a reduction in wages was needed to save the coal-mining industry. It was not a climate which promised new opportunities for women in engineering. After two years in Devon she may have seen enough of rural electrification to feel that managing a small power station in the country was not her greatest ambition.

Beatrice's good fortune was that Margaret Partridge was not only her employer and teacher, she was a friend. She believed that Beatrice was capable of taking a degree in engineering, and with the help of the Women's Engineering Society and Miss Rowbotham, set about preparing her for entry. Miss Rowbotham's part was to bring her applied maths up to standard; the WES were able to recommend and support an application to the London and National Society for Women's Service for an interest-free loan to help pay her tuition fees. No universities offered scholarships to women to study engineering in 1929, Beatrice wrote later, in an article on her first ten years as an engineer, and the loan of £1000 gave her the resources to apply to the Victoria University of Manchester.

She was accepted by the Department of Electrical Engineering, to start in Manchester in October 1929. The entrants that year seem to have been a lively group, and included two women, the first of their sex to study engineering at the University. They were Beatrice, now twenty years old, and Sheila McGuffie, three months short of her eighteenth birthday. Sheila was a "home student", walking a mile to her local station each day before taking a train into the city; for Beatrice it was back to "digs" and the spartan domestic arrangements that she was used to. They became friends and gave each other moral support during the first unfamiliar weeks until they got to know their co-students. "I remember George Kenyon (one of the new intake) as a "hefty" student and always good humoured as were all our year." Sheila McGuffie wrote later: "The staff certainly were anxious that we should understand their lectures".

The staff also encouraged them to attend lectures in subjects outside their faculty, which allowed Beatrice to study mechanical engineering and thermodynamics as well as electrical subjects. The "good humoured" young men made sure that the girls enjoyed their subject lectures by extracting some of the lead shot from the counterweights of the lecture room lights, and forcing it down the back of their necks while they were trying to listen to the lecturer.

Beatrice and Sheila McGuffie had different sporting interests. Sheila played hockey and lacrosse; Beatrice joined a motorcycle club and competed in trials in the Peak District. She bought a

Matchless Model V/2 – a 495cc overhead valve machine described as the "Super Sports," and rode in the solo and sidecar classes. Sheila enterprisingly rode as sidecar passenger in one trial, but was too light to keep the sidecar wheel down.

Beatrice was not interested in fashionable clothes or eating out at restaurants, nor was she a lover of music or the theatre. However she was becoming a heavy smoker, and any kind of motor sport entails many expenses beyond a competitive machine. Her loan from the National Society for Women's Service was invested in tuition fees so her parents were clearly generous in their support of her living costs. In Spring of her second year at Manchester she arranged a summer holiday job, which she hoped would be instructive as well as paying some of her expenses.

It was in the Transformer Department of Ferranti Ltd in Hollinwood, where she worked for eight weeks. One of the very few women working on the shop floor at Ferranti was called on to "show Beatrice the ropes". Her name was Muriel Shephard, she was close to Beatrice in age, and the two quickly became good friends. Working conditions at Ferranti were terrible (as they remained in most engineering works for another thirty years), and the presence of women was resented. Unemployment was rising and the government of Ramsey MacDonald was considering a cut in unemployment benefit to help solve the financial crisis of 1931. In this forbidding atmosphere Beatrice and Muriel found that they had at least two things in common – a love of motorcycles and an ironic sense of humour. Beatrice discovered that Muriel was studying maths and physics at night school and offered to coach her; Muriel, who was nineteen, asked her mother if Beatrice could stay in their house on Victoria Road, Whalley Range, in South Manchester, and Mrs Shephard agreed.

Muriel had a younger sister, Dorothy, or

"Dot", as she was called, and the Victoria Road household as she describes it was a lively one before and after Beatrice joined it. The house was large, with a garden which was Mr Shephard's pride and joy. An airgun was kept in the upstairs lavatory to discourage visiting cats, or to practice target shooting at Craven "A" cigarette packets pinned to an archway in the garden. The aspiring engineers shared a large upstairs room with a small cooker, so Muriel and Beatrice ate separately from the family except for Sunday evenings when everyone ate together and then played Monopoly or other games. Otherwise they lived in their room and cooked, slept, studied, worked on motorcycle bits and, in Dorothy's words, "smoked like Mexican bandits".

The Shephard household was home for Beatrice for most of her time at Manchester University. She graduated in 1932 and her year did particularly well afterwards. One of her year, George Kenyon, was knighted in 1976 and Chairman of Council of Manchester University for many years; he remembered both his intake and Beatrice with pleasure:

"The group who graduated in 1932 turned out to be a pretty good lot and I've always been proud to be one of them." Of Beatrice: *"Beatrice was always good fun and startled us with her exploits on her large and powerful motor bike. I once rode pillion with her – the only time in my life – into central Manchester and back along Oxford Road. It was an alarming experience before there were speed limits . . . but she handled it with great skill."*

Two other 1932 graduates were also later knighted, and both Beatrice and Sheila McGuffie eventually overcame male prejudice enough to play important roles as engineers during the Second World War.

After graduating with honours in Electrical Engineering, Beatrice started studying for a Master of Science in Mechanical Engineering, her true passion. She chose research into working temperatures of pistons in different types in diesel engine, and received a grant to work with a lecturer who specialised in IC (Ignition-Compression or two-stroke) engines. The grant from the Department of Engineering recognised her exceptional ability; money for grants was limited at a time of reduced government spending and still growing unemployment.

Poor Muriel lost her job at Ferranti; having clocked on late twice she knew that a third time would mean automatic dismissal. When late a third time she rode her motorcycle right through the workshop to clock in, finishing her job with a bang, not a whimper. There was still a place for Beatrice in the Shephard household. With her help Muriel found work with one of Margaret Partridge's companies, and continued to study for an electrical diploma at night school, with more coaching from her room-mate. Muriel later told her daughter that Beatrice could not understand that anyone could have difficulty in grasping the finer points of mathematics and thermodynamics, and lost her temper with her more than once. Her daughter, Biddy Fraser-Davies, wondered if the bond between the two was an attraction of opposites, as Muriel was not the intellectual giant that Beatrice appeared to be. But Muriel was determined and spirited, as active as Beatrice in fighting for women's right to do what they wanted to do, rather than what was considered acceptable – and as ready to have fun and make mischief.

Both of them liked practical jokes and once tried to alarm the Shephards by producing what seemed to be B's severed finger. Younger sister Dorothy was not impressed. Then they set up a poker game in their shared all-purpose living room and put all the money they could muster on the table, to persuade Muriel's parents that they were heavy gamblers. Perhaps the older generation was more easily duped than the younger, but Beatrice appreciated Dorothy's company and sometimes took her with her to the laboratory in the Department of Mechanical Engineering when she had research to do on her own and wanted someone to talk to.

The job situation was still desperate in December 1933, when Beatrice received her degree of Master of Science. What could she do? Staff of the Engineering Department were aware of her predicament, and it was a sign of their admiration of her work that Dr G. F. Mucklow, lecturer in engineering, obtained permission and money to take her on as assistant in his own research project. This was an ongoing investigation into various aspects of the behaviour of supercharged single cylinder engines, on which he had published a paper in the Proceedings of the Institution of Mechanical Engineering in 1932. Working at Manchester University and using single cylinder engines provided by Rolls-Royce and Napier, he had looked at the influence of different supercharger pressures and compression ratios on horsepower, heat losses and fuel consumption. (Development work on single cylinder engines was routinely carried out by aircraft and automobile manufacturers before building a prototype of a new multi-cylinder engine.)

In 1933 he was working on the effects of varying valve timing on a supercharged engine. This was a long drawn-out study which took second place to Dr Mucklow's teaching duties. Beatrice's contribution to this research was to be both academic and practical. Beside taking readings and analysing them, she constructed parts for the test apparatus, and maintained, set and repaired the engines and superchargers, using welding and brazing equipment and lathes and other tools in the Department's workshop. The practice was just what Beatrice wanted for her newest interest – motorcycle racing. Not just racing but also the preparation and improvement of her own racing machine.

Late in 1933 or more probably early in 1934 she bought a model 30 overhead-camshaft 490cc Norton, a second hand machine which would have cost her around £70. How she could afford it at this particular time is something of an enigma, but no doubt she traded in her Matchless, and as Anne, her sister said, when someone really wants something, they find the money somewhere. The Norton was to be used for racing, a completely new venture for Beatrice, and specifically for racing at the track at Brooklands at Weybridge in Surrey.

Bampton in Devon, where Beatrice first worked as an apprentice in Miss Partridge's electricity company. The wiring still looks a bit primitive.

The Electrical Engineering class of 1929 at Manchester University with Beatrice (on right) and Sheila McGuffie in front. *Dr T. E. Broadbent*

Women workers at a Vickers munition factory during World War One. The Women's
Engineering Society fought against dismissal of women from factories after the end of the war.
Science and Society Picture Library, Science Museum London.

"Perpetrators of the Original Offence." Members of the Women's Engineering Society who
achieved a change in the Convention governing the employment of women at night. Beatrice,
looking very shy, is second from the left. She broke the Convention to force a test case. *Women's
Engineering Society*

Muriel Shephard, friend and fellow motorcyclist, on her AJS sports model. She has a kitten on her lap. *Elizabeth Fraser-Davies*

Beatrice with her Matchless V/2, the 1928 sports model. It shows
signs of its use in Peak District trials. Beatrice did not believe in too
much spit and polish. *Anne and Dennis Lock*

Beatrice gowned for graduation to Batchelor of Science in 1932. *Anne and Dennis Lock*

Three

Brooklands

When Beatrice decided to move on from motorcycle trials to motorcycle racing, Brooklands was her obvious choice of racetrack. It was close to home, it was designed for pure speed, and it demanded courage and strength of a rider, rather than the experience and circuit knowledge needed for the Isle of Man TT.

This extraordinary race course was built in the Surrey countryside by Mr HF Locke King, the leading local landowner and a motoring enthusiast. Its construction started in 1906, in which year motor racing was in full swing on the public roads of the continent, but forbidden by law on those of Great Britain. In that year a French car reached a record speed of 108 mph on a French public road. In England the speed limit was twelve miles per hour. Locke King was determined to correct this handicap to the development of British cars and the national motor industry.

Brooklands Motor Course opened in June 1907, and, surfaced with concrete, it consisted of two straights, one slightly kinked, joined by two long semi-circular bends with banking high enough to be seen from almost any point on the track. Three and a quarter miles in length, it was designed to be "safe" at an average speed of 120 mph, and it soon became the centre of motor racing and record breaking in Great Britain. It became extremely popular with racing drivers and motorcyclists, with a good atmosphere of friendly but intense rivalry. It was less popular than hoped for with the public, but those who came and enjoyed it took comfort from the Brooklands catchphrase – "the right

crowd and no crowding."

By 1934 the track had lost the smooth white concrete finish it had in 1907, being extensively patched where the frequent passage of hefty racing cars (some of them, such as the original "Chitty I", powered by aero engines of over 20 litres capacity) had broken up the surface, while settling of the course where the banking crossed the River Wey created dips and rises that launched the fastest competitors clear of the track. Strength and concentration were needed to hold a machine to the best line for the fastest lap possible, specially in the case of contenders for the lap record, who had to race close to the top of the banking.

Beatrice first came to Brooklands in June 1934. With her she brought the 490cc overhead camshaft Norton that was to be her racing mount and everyday transport for the next fourteen years. Beatrice's work on experimental engines in the Engineering Department at Manchester University sharpened her skills with machine tools and welding equipment. At the same time she was learning how to improve the flow of gas, and she had applied these lessons to her motorcycle in the hope of making a respectable showing. In racing trim, the Norton was stripped of anything not needed on the track, and therefore could not be ridden on the road, so while at University, Beatrice had to load the machine into the guards' van of the London train at Manchester and push it between stations in London to take the train to Weybridge and Brooklands.

Her first event was a mid-week meeting for new members of the British Motor Cycle Racing Club Beatrice's performance earned an enthusiastic write-up in the *Motor Cycle* magazine of June 14th., 1934. *"The fair sex struck another blow for recognition when Miss B. Shilling, who had done only about three practice laps in her life, finished sixth in her very first race and third in her second, lapping at over 90 mph on a Norton tuned by herself. An M.Sc. of Manchester University, she had even made the pattern for casting of the elaborate aluminium fishtail, then finished the casting to shape!"* (This was part of the exhaust silencer required by Brooklands regulations to appease close neighbours of the track.)

Beatrice's second race on the same day was another newcomers' event, and this she won outright: after only two events she was ready to take on the "regulars" – the experienced professional and semi-professional riders who made Brooklands their base of operations. There were not many in this little band, but they included gifted and very serious engine builders, such as Francis Beart, Eric Fernihough and Ben Bickell, a few top TT riders like Les Archer, Jock West and Johnny Lockett, and a few with riding skill and an irrepressible sense of fun who were happy to ride whatever was offered.

One of these was Charles Mortimer, who wrote his memories of Brooklands forty years after the last race there. He describes coaching a young lady "who was really a very trim and competent rider", to achieve a lap at over 100 mph during practice for the races. 100 mph was a magical figure for newcomers, and an officially timed lap of this speed during a race earned the rider a highly-prized trophy, the British Motorcycle Racing Club's "Brooklands Gold Star". Although this was only a small lapel badge, and certainly not made of gold, it was a generally recognised sign that its wearer had graduated to the ranks of expert track riders.

Mortimer had a theory that feelings of awe of the magic 100 mph acted as a barrier to new riders' actual achievement of that speed, and he claimed that by signalling to the rider during practice a lower lap speed than they had actually done; say 98 mph when in fact they had circulated at 99 mph, the rider would be spurred to hang on tight and open the throttle a bit more and thus speed through the 100 mph barrier without realising it! Charles Mortimer did not name the "trim and competent" lady, but it can only have been one of the two women racing at Brooklands in the mid 1930s, Fanny Blenkiron or Beatrice Shilling. Both of them were small, competent and determined.

Beatrice had no need of this well-intended help, as she was highly motivated, and rode a very fast machine. Her next competition was "Hutchinson 100 Day" at Brooklands, on August 24th, a day of races which offered enough prize money to attract almost all the "regulars", and Beatrice entered two of the events, all of which were handicaps. At Brooklands this meant that "Ebby" Ebblewhite, the all-knowing resident handicapper, gave each rider a starting time according to his estimate of their potential, the slowest starting first, and the fastest starting on "scratch" – in other words after everyone else had set off. All the riders would form a single line across the wide Railway straight, and "Ebby" would send them off according to his handicap. As 175cc machines competed against 1000cc bikes, the handicap between the fastest and the slowest could give the first rider to start time enough to complete a whole lap and pass the start line again before the "scratch" man roared into the fray. If his estimate had ever been spot on for each competitor, every rider would have passed the finishing line simultaneously, but Ebblewhite's predictions were usually upset by mechanical problems and crafty riders.

Beatrice was among the first starters in this three lap race; after a steady first lap she took her Norton firmly in hand and lapped at over 100 mph. *Motor Cycling's* reporter was impressed:

"A feature of the first handicap was the brilliant riding of Miss B. Shilling on a very standard-looking 490cc Norton. After a slowish first lap, she made up for lost time with a second circuit of 101.02 mph, thus joining the select ranks of Gold Star holders, being the second woman motorcycle racer to do so."

"Ebby" promptly re-handicapped Beatrice for the next race, "penalising" her 9 seconds for her new turn of speed. She thus earned, as Motor Cycling put it, "the distinction of being the first woman to be put on scratch in a competition with men at Brooklands."

She lapped still faster in the next race, 101.85 mph. She must have been very happy and very proud on that hot August day. She had successfully transformed her standard motorcycle into a racer whose speed impressed professional riders, and she had shown herself to be as tough and resourceful as any man at Brooklands. It was a triumph that she could share in full with Muriel Shephard, her Manchester room-mate, and it was an engineering success that would be appreciated by Dr Mucklow, who had once worked on racing car engines himself.

Although Brooklands is sometimes associated with wealthy young men with Bentleys and Lagondas, almost characters from P. G. Wodehouse, who named their cars "Chitty-Bang-Bang" and "Softly-Catch-Monkey", snobbery and sexual discrimination were the exception at the track. Leaving aside well-supported "Ladies races", women were among the most successful record breakers and race competitors from 1920 on. The Outer Circuit lap record for two litre cars still stands in Mrs. Gwenda Stewart's name at 135.95 mph, after she displaced Kay Petre (who raced cars ranging from a supercharged Austin Seven to a ten litre

Delage) as fastest lady on the track.

There were fewer women motorcyclists, but they also raced without prejudice. Gwenda Stewart (then Gwenda Janson), was one of the first in 1922, while the first woman to gain a 100 mph Gold Star was Fanny Blenkiron, in April 1934. Like Beatrice, Miss Blenkiron was short and able to flatten herself on the machine to reduce wind resistance. Petrol tank tops were well padded to save teeth from being broken when passing over one of Brooklands' many bumps.

Unfortunately we do not know what changes Beatrice made to the engine of her Norton, although it is very likely that she kept notes of all modifications. She later told friends at the Royal Aircraft Establishment that she had tried different lengths of inlet tract, but we can be sure that other improvements were made in her workshop during winter 1935-6. In fact her main workshop was the large room in the house on Victoria Road, Manchester, that she shared with Muriel Shephard, but she was also allowed to use the Engineering Department's workshop at the University.

Fresh modifications to the Norton that winter produced outstanding results. A full programme of racing in 1935 started in May with a third place to Jock West and Noel Pope, followed by a win for Beatrice's Norton in the hands of H.C. Lamacraft, an experienced Brooklands hand. Jock West, who raced for the Vincent, BMW and AJS factories in TT races, as well as against Beatrice at Brooklands on his own Triumph, describes the friendly competition between riders: "At Brooklands in pre-war days everybody knew everybody so I suppose I knew Miss Shilling as well as anyone." Machines were lent to friends or made available by professionals like Francis Beart on some financial arrangement.

On July 4 *Motor Cycle* magazine

reported:

"From the 33 second mark Miss Shilling on her self-tuned Norton ran through the field, and with one lap at 101.64 m.p.h. and one lap at 102.69, provided a somewhat unexpected win."

Unexpected, because second finisher was Ben Bickell, supercharged Ariel four, and third was Noel Pope, supercharged Brough Superior, each of them professional riders and track lap record holders in the 500cc and Unlimited classes respectively.

Away from Brooklands, Beatrice was faced with the need to find suitable work when her research assistantship at Manchester ended later in the year. Although the worst of the Depression had passed, jobs for men in engineering, aircraft or automobile companies were scarce; for women they were nonexistent. In spite of the advances made by the Women's Engineering Society, the idea of women engineers on the shop floor was generally anathema to the captains of industry. In the research establishments of the Admiralty and the Air Ministry women scientists had achieved some recognition, and it was to these organisations that Beatrice applied.

She kept copies of her letters of application and the Ministries' replies. Beatrice travelled up and down the main line between Manchester and London for a series of interviews – candidates were required to bear any travelling costs – and waited outside rooms on long corridors to be questioned by a panel of bored-sounding men. At one interview the subject of her Brooklands successes came up: "I suppose the men let you win," remarked of one of her interviewers. Her reaction was simple – laughter.

Beatrice's efforts to find employment extended from June 1935 to March 1936. Her ambition was to work in research on aero-engines, but first she had to disentangle the complex system of titles and grades of the Scientific Civil Service to apply for a level which gave her the best chance of acceptance, while offering a challenging and remunerative career. Visits to London for interview cost Beatrice both the rail fare and a day's pay as a research assistant, which meant less money for motorcycle racing. On receipt of yet another pompously-phrased rejection, which opened "Sir" in spite of being addressed to Miss B. Shilling, her frustration turned to fury and Beatrice scored out the "Sir" and wrote "Lady! to you" in its place.

The racing at Brooklands was going well, however, and Beatrice often had good company at the track to give encouragement, push off her Norton at the start of races and generally add to the enjoyment of the day. Muriel Shephard's boyfriend, Desmond Breed, later to marry her, was the ideal "pusher off", large and enthusiastic. Anne, Beatrice's sister and at that time a professional dancer, sometimes came as well and attracted the attention of the young men who raced cars or flew from the airfield that was enclosed within the Brooklands bowl. Anne was invited by one young man to go up in his aeroplane and, uncertain of his competence, she asked her sister's advice. Beatrice's reply was typically laconic: "Take a parachute." The young man flew alone.

1935 was Beatrice's best year in motorcycle racing. Competing with the very best of the regular riders, she became the fastest woman ever to circulate Brooklands on a motorcycle, at 106 mph. Norton Motors wrote to congratulate her on winning her race on Hutchinson 100 Day. "We regard this as a very remarkable performance and indicates your prowess in the handling of your NORTON machine", and asked if they could have a photograph of her on her machine for their 1936 brochure. This was supplied and appeared on a page devoted to international racing successes.

The posed picture shows her perched on the machine with a happy expression, blonde hair in a bob and feet just reaching the ground.

The year ended without a job. Yet another application was in the pipeline, this time direct to the Royal Aircraft Establishment at Farnborough, the national centre of aeronautical research. On the motorcycle front, *Motor Cycle* magazine reported that Beatrice was planning to supercharge her Norton; she knew the potential power increase that compressing the air-fuel mixture could give, but was not yet ready to carry out the major alterations that this would need.

Finding work was now the greatest priority and correspondence with the Admiralty and Air Ministry continued through the winter. On March 5th, 1936 Beatrice finally received an offer from the Air Ministry of employment at the Royal Aircraft Establishment at Farnborough. The offer was subject to a medical examination at her own expense, it was not the job in aero-engine research that she wanted, but it was at the right place and Beatrice did not intend to sit back once she got there.

She started work in April. Soon after starting there she met met George Naylor, a mathematician working in the Mechanical Test Department. Brenda Rimmer, another recent recruit to the Establishment in 1936, remembers the day when she believes that their acquaintance became something more.

"Bea and George Naylor and I were attending evening classes in aerodynamics at Farnborough Technical School. George lived near me and one evening he took me there on the back of his motor bike – the only time in my life I was ever on the back of a bike. We all sat together and during the mid-session break we went outside for a smoke. George and Bea didn't come back into class and I went home by bus. Shortly after this they were married and I

have always thought it was set up that evening."

George raced motorcycles and was also a competent mechanic. He was well over six feet tall, towering over Beatrice at just five feet one and a quarter inches, and when racing started at Brooklands in 1937, George came as well. George and Beatrice both raced the Norton at Brooklands, after George had served an apprenticeship as assistant mechanic and pusher. Although both lived near Farnborough and therefore quite close to Brooklands, work prevented regular racing and neither equalled Beatrice's earlier successes. George did not gain his Gold Star until 1938, and the story is that so far from gently coaching him, as Charles Mortimer seems to have done for her, Beatrice just told George that she would marry him when he got his Star, not until. The Gold Star achieved, they were married with a minimum of fuss and very few guests at Aldershot Registry Office on July 21st, 1938.

In autumn and winter of 1938-39 the Norton was stripped down and rebuilt as a new machine. The photograph of this hybrid will help to clarify the description that follows. A home-made supercharger was mounted above the engine sprocket and driven by chain from the crankshaft. The petrol tank was converted into a compressed air chamber to maintain pressure between supercharger and carburettor. Beatrice fabricated a new fuel tank and placed it exactly where the saddle had been situated, leaving the seat perched on top of the mudguard above the rear wheel centre. The carburettor remained attached to the cylinder head in its normal place. Fuel fed into this as usual, while the air compressed by the supercharger entered the bell-mouth of the carburettor and forced the mixture into the engine. This arrangement had worked well in the supercharged single cylinder tests that Beatrice had carried out at Manchester with Dr Mucklow.

The repositioning of saddle and fuel tank

on the Norton put the seat too far back for Beatrice to reach the handlebars, so George was nominated rider. Once fired up and on the track there were many problems. Use of a centrifugal supercharger deprived the engine of its flexibility, and the decision to blow air through the carburettor instead of mounting the carburettor at the inlet side of the supercharger necessitated elaborate balancing pipework to avoid blowing fuel back into the tank. With stiff springing of the front wheel and none at the rear, Beatrice and George both admitted to finding the Norton a frightening machine at lap speeds of around and over 100 mph, though both still loved the excitement of close racing.

In Brooklands' last year of existence as a race track, Beatrice and George enjoyed a much fuller season than in 1937 and 1938. George seems to have done most of the riding but "Miss B. Shilling" entered him in every race and undoubtedly gave robust advice on tactics and engine care. Without the supercharger George won a wet three lap race on April 1st, 1938, at 99.41 mph, a clear demonstration of his courage in bad conditions. With the supercharger

George was unplaced in races in June and July, and this version never ran well enough to challenge the supercharged Triumphs and Ariels that raced in 1939. This was disappointing as he had hopes of breaking the 500cc Outer Circuit lap record, which would have needed a lap speed of close to 120 mph. Like Velocette in 1931-2 and Vincent-H.R.D. in 1936, Beatrice found that supercharging a racing single cylinder engine led to one problem after another, and the theoretical jump in performance was seldom realised. A rare exception was the 250cc Moto Guzzi built by the Italian factory for the 1939 Grand Prix season, which won the European Championship that year.

The declaration of war in September 1939 ended racing at Brooklands for ever. Beatrice and George became fully occupied with war work at the Royal Aircraft Establishment, and the well-raced Norton was returned to a road machine, to become Beatrice's chief means of transport for the next fourteen years.

At Brooklands, doing something photogenic for the camera. *Anne and Dennis Lock*

Posing with her Norton for a publicity photograph used in the 1935 Norton catalogue. Beatrice tuned the engine to make it one of the fastest machines in its class. *Anne and Dennis Lock*

The real thing; 1935 Cup Day, with Beatrice, who won the race, almost completely hidden by the Morgan of Rhodes. Her Norton's tank is just visible. Nearest the camera, Ben Bickell, Ariel, then Noel Pope, supercharged Brough Superior, Jock West, Triumph and Rhodes.

The Brooklands Regulars. Francis Beart, Joe Forbes, Charles Mortimer (standing), Frank Baker, and Noel Pope, who took the lap record for motorcycles at 124.51 mph in 1938 on his supercharged Brough.

1938. Beatrice, second from the camera, looks utterly relaxed before a race in which she was not highly placed. In the distance the steep banking over which the race will pass can be seen.

The supercharged version of the Norton devised by Beatrice, showing the air blower feeding into the petrol tank, now serving as a compressed air reservoir. George Naylor, sitting behind the uncomfortable-looking new fuel tank, was tall enough to reach the handlebars, but Beatrice was not.

Four

The Royal Aircraft Establishment

On April 25th 1936, Beatrice reported for work as a Technical Author at the Farnborough branch of the Air Ministry's Technical Publications Department. She regarded this as a staging post to the Royal Aircraft Establishment, where she looked forward to working on aero-engine research and development.

A new sense of purpose was beginning to move through the Establishment, as the Government had reluctantly recognised the threat of German militarism in 1935, and had drawn up plans for rearmament in which the Air Ministry was to play a major part. The Establishment had a long and distinguished history of development and manufacture of all kinds of aircraft. It started with the commissioning in 1878 by the War Office of a Balloon Equipment Store and Balloon School at the Woolwich Arsenal, which outgrew its premises, moving first to Chatham, then Aldershot, and finally to Farnborough in 1905. The early superintendents of the factory were flight enthusiasts, who were quite willing to be persuaded by pioneers of powered flight, such as SF Cody and JW Dunne, to experiment with man-carrying kites, powered dirigibles and aeroplanes.

By 1914 the War Office had come to approve and finance not only the design and construction of aeroplanes at Farnborough but also engine development, structural testing of airframes, instruments, armaments, electrical and wireless installations. Now named the Royal Aircraft Factory, the establishment greatly expanded these activities during the First World War,

producing from its own designs and research the prototype S.E.5 fighter plane that became the dominant British fighter in the last two years of the war. 5000 men and women were working at Farnborough as scientists, technical staff, test pilots or administrators by 1915.

After objections by private manufacturers (supported by a strong press campaign) that the Royal Aircraft Factory was exploiting its War Office connections to create a monopoly in the building of fighter aircraft, the Factory stopped building aircraft. It concentrated on scientific work, building two wind tunnels and enlarging the range of work on engines, structures, metallurgy and instrumentation. New equipment, and test flying brought improvements in aerodynamics and structures that made Britain a leader in the advancement of powered flight.

After the end of the War in 1918, activities were rather quickly run down, mainly for reasons of national economy. The Establishment had been renamed, in June 1918, the Royal Aircraft Establishment in deference to the newly created Royal Air Force; two RAFs could not exist side by side. Work continued in all the departments created between 1914 and 1918, but staffing dropped to around 1000 and the pace of progress slowed down dramatically in the 1920s. Government stringency dictated by the Depression and its effects continued into the 1930s. However, Japanese militarism and disturbing political changes in Europe, with an openly aggressive stance by Germany and Italy, forced the government to reconsider its policy of minimal spending on defence.

These developments may well have helped Beatrice to find work at the RAE, as recruitment was increased to strengthen its role in British rearmament. But Beatrice was given work unrelated to warlike preparations – work that as a graduate mechanical engineer she found uninspiring. Furthermore she was to start not at the main RAE. site, where research installations crowded to the north-east of the Establishment airfield, but at the Technical Publications Department at the Old Post Office in Farnborough.

Among the tasks of this department was the writing and revision of aircraft and aero-engine manuals. These were thick volumes, running to over 400 pages. The engine versions contained technical descriptions and detailed instructions for starting, running and fully dismantling and rebuilding engines. As a technical author Beatrice was told to revise the manual for the Bristol Pegasus II, type M3, which was a 1934 version of the long stroke (7 ½") nine cylinder radial engine introduced in 1932.

Beatrice later said that her six months in Technical Publications were boring, even unhappy times. For a practical engineer who was keen to start contributing to engine development, her work must have been unsatisfying, but it took her to the Bristol Aeroplane Company's engine factory in Patchway, Bristol, to see engines being assembled and tested. Beatrice admitted to finding the bench testing of engines very impressive; safety at work did not run to ear protectors or sound insulation, and the noise of a Pegasus at maximum revs, from close to, must have been shattering. It was an engine with a notable record of success. It powered the fastest twin engined aircraft of the RAF in 1936, the Boulton Paul Overstrand bomber, as well as the single engined Vickers Vildebeest, a biplane torpedo bomber that was still in service in the Far East in 1940. During her stay of several weeks in Bristol,

Beatrice also saw the sleeve valve engines that Roy Fedden, Chief Engineer of the Engine Division, believed were the aero-engines of the future.

Some excitement was given to her stay at Patchway by the fact that Fedden did not tolerate women inside his factory, and Beatrice recalled that she was whisked out of sight when he was known to be close by. The resident Technical Officer, who checked engine parts for compliance with Air Ministry requirements, arranged for her to be driven to the Bristol Aircraft Division, just up the road, where women did work, for lunch and use of the facilities.

It is a shame that Fedden and Beatrice did not meet then, as once Fedden had recovered from the shock of seeing a woman next to one of his engines, he might have recognised single-mindedness and determination to match his own. (They met toward the end of the war on R.A.E. business.) Beatrice completed the Pegasus manual with details of reassembly, such as immersion of connecting rods in hot oil (up to 300°C) to allow a pre-cooled new bush to be inserted. She told a reporter after the war that while she was working at Technical Publications she issued a leaflet on renewal of Pegasus valve seats, in which she recommended aircraft fitters to stop a passing Walls ice-cream salesman to get frozen CO_2 ("dry ice") to cool the valve seat for insertion in the cylinder head. The leaflet went out without being checked and there was "a big row" when it was seen by senior staff.

Beatrice was insistent in her requests for a transfer to aero-engine work, and in October 1936 she moved to the main part of the RAE, the "Factory Site" as it continued to be called long after the original factory was closed, to join the Carburettor Section of Engine Experimental Department, later called simply Engine Department.

Engine research was led by Dr AA

Griffith, a man with great practical and inventive gifts, who had worked at Farnborough since 1914 and was appointed head of Engine Department in 1938. In 1926 he had published a paper on "An Aerodynamic Theory of Turbine Design", a precursor to the work that produced the jet engine, and among his later proposals was a pressure injection carburettor, a prototype of which was built and tested in 1934 before Griffith moved on to new work.

The function of a carburettor is to meter fuel and mix it with air to give the right mixture and volume for the work that an engine is being asked to do, be it cruising, accelerating or climbing at maximum power. In a car, which spends its life on the ground, atmospheric pressure is constant, more or less, the range of air temperature is small and the car stays on a horizontal plane. For aircraft, carburettor design must allow for more extreme changes in operating conditions.

In flight, atmospheric pressure and air temperature drop dramatically as altitude increases, altering the density of the air-fuel mixture. Most fighter aircraft engines had superchargers to compress the mixture and increase power, and these had variable rates of boost. Finally the aerobatic manoeuvres of attack and evasion in combat subjected the fuel supply to "g" forces. All of these variables had to be considered in the design of an aero-engine carburettor. Compensating mechanisms, whether manual or automatic, were needed to provide the best fuel mixture for every situation.

Beatrice started in the Engine Experimental Department under the supervision of WC Clothier, head of carburettor work. Two of Clothier's special interests were the development of the injection carburettor, and the prevention of carburettor icing. Icing most commonly occurred when part of the fuel sucked into the intake airstream

hit the throttle and evaporated, cooling the throttle enough to freeze the moisture in humid air. The resulting ice constricted the air passage round the throttles and could freeze the throttle solid. In certain conditions icing can affect a motorcycle carburettor in air temperatures above 0°C. At 20,000 feet altitude the temperature is normally -30°C or lower, so positive prevention of icing is essential.

Clothier designed a glass carburettor to demonstrate the formation of ice in a carburettor; he also offered solutions to the problem, one of them being injection of a small amount of alcohol into the fuel system at the float chamber. Neither Clothier nor Beatrice suffered fools gladly and the two worked well together, becoming friends. Beatrice helped him with his work on the injection carburettor, investigating ways to automate the adjustments for supercharger boost and air pressure. In 1937 there were still aircraft in which these adjustments were made with levers by the pilot, who was already busy controlling airspeed and direction, while navigating and looking out for the enemy.

Developments of the injection or RAE carburettor were tested by Beatrice on Bristol radial engines – the poppet valve Mercury, and the sleeve valve Perseus, as these had quite different valve timing and gas flow characteristics. The Mercury tests were carried out on a tethered aircraft, a Gloster Gauntlet, while the Perseus tests were done on a test bed. When poor running or breakages occurred, modifications or repairs, including work on the test equipment, were done in the workshops, some by Beatrice herself, until a satisfactory result was obtained.

Clothier and Beatrice reported on their work on the RAE carburettor in a "Note" (No. E. 3587), dated October 1937. Changes included improvement of response to boost pressure changes and to changes in air pressure due to altitude.

Control of low engine speeds, at which the servo boost control was too sensitive and produced "hunting" – uncontrollable rising and falling of engine speed – was returned to direct pilot control. Under "Further Developments", the Note recorded a request by the Bristol Aeroplane Company for a "tentative design" of an R.A.E. carburettor for its new Hercules engine. This was an exciting request; this magnificent two-row radial engine, with fourteen cylinders and sleeve valves, had a capacity of over 38 litres, and was to develop 1,375 bhp in Mk 1 form, more than any other production aero-engine.

By late 1937 the Hercules engine was being flight tested. Yet it was 1940 before Hercules-engined Bristol Beaufighters were delivered to RAF squadrons. This was not because of any weakness of Bristol's Engine Department: far from it. Any new engine reveals problems in design as full testing proceeds, and the Hercules was a powerful engine whose sleeve valves required close engineering tolerances. Metal fatigue, lubrication failings, and vibration must all be traced and fully corrected before an engine can be released for service trials, then production. In addition Bristol Engine Department planned to wind up manufacture of the Pegasus and Mercury engines in readiness for a war which Fedden was certain would break out.

Beatrice and a colleague, D Ramsey, set to work on a special version of the RAE carburettor for the Hercules, and they too found problems which needed solving. The low-speed control problem reappeared; hard acceleration produced a back-fire; the automatic cut-off valve cut off when it should not have done. Progress was delayed by the need to share the test engine with other sections. A satisfactory RAE Hercules carburettor was not ready until late in 1940, but then it produced excellent acceleration from low to maximum engine speed. More

testing was now necessary before the design would be ready for series production, then every component would need Ministry of Air Production approval before manufacture could start.

By then Beatrice's professional gifts had been recognised. She could identify the physical laws involved in a new problem or requirement, quantify them and design a mechanical solution. She could also design the tests that ensured that the instrument or engine performed as intended, and if not, why not. She was devoted to her work and got on well with any serious-minded colleague. In August 1937 Beatrice was promoted from Assistant III to Assistant II.

Beatrice kept the letter from the Chief Superintendent, R.A.E. which gave her the news:

"5th August, 1937.

I have to inform you of your selection to fill, in an acting capacity, an Assistant II post in the Engine Experimental Department. The promotion takes effect from 10th July, 1937, from which date you will be paid at the salary of £250 a year, and on 20th April, 1938, i.e. the second anniversary of your entry into Government service, you will be paid at the rate of £265 a year on the scale £265 x 12 - £315.

Your future incremental date will be 20th April.

p.p. Chief Superintendent, R.A.E."

This was exactly the job that Beatrice had applied for back in June 1935; she was where she wanted to be, but this elegantly-phrased letter sowed the seeds of a lasting lack of confidence in the fairness of the RAE's administrators. Beatrice replied to the letter in her usual economic style:

"Sir, *Vacancy 390/429A – Assistant Grade 11 August, 1937*

I beg to acknowledge with thanks your letter, referring to the above, dated 5th

August informing me of my selection to fill one of the above posts.

The commencing salary of £250 per annum quoted in your letter disagrees with the advertised salary of £265 - 12 - 315.

May I be informed of the cause of this discrepancy.

Your obedient servant. B. Shilling"

The administration's answer illustrated the oriental complexity of grades, status and salaries operating in the RAE:

"With reference to your letter of the 20th August 1937, there was an error in your starting salary which will be £260 p.a. The reason you start at less than the minimum of the grade advertised is that the Air Ministry has decided that its employees must be two years as Civil Servants or, alternatively, one year in the grade to which they are promoted before they can receive an increment exceeding £50."

AH Hall, the Chief Superintendent, signed this letter himself. He made no suggestion that he was Beatrice's obedient servant. Beatrice let matters rest on this point, but it was the first of many similar exchanges.

Beatrice received two further promotions in the following two years, the first was to Assistant I, in June 1938, a month after Austria welcomed Hitler and became part of the "New Germany", and three months before the meeting in Munich at which Britain and France agreed to allow Germany to occupy Czechoslovakia. Some historians argue that the Munich agreement was an allied gambit to buy time, rather than a genuine hope for peace in Europe. During the next twelve months both sides threw themselves into arms manufacture and the organisation of defences.

On November 1st 1939, Beatrice was promoted to Technical Officer in charge of carburettor research and development work. Britain had declared war on Germany on September 3rd after Germany invaded Poland in defiance of a mutual defence alliance between Poland, Great Britain and France. The war which Prime Minister Neville Chamberlain had done his best to prevent was on.

The Bristol Pegasus II M3 nine cylinder radial engine. The Pegasus engine was launched in 1932 and, in various forms, was fitted to a very wide range of fighting and civil aircraft. Beatrice re-wrote the official *Air Publication* for this power plant in 1936. *Rolls-Royce Heritage Trust, Bristol*

Detail of the Pegasus valve gear. The long tubes each contain two pushrods. One pushrod operates the two inlet valves for each cylinder – the other, two exhaust valves. *Rolls-Royce Heritage Trust, Bristol*

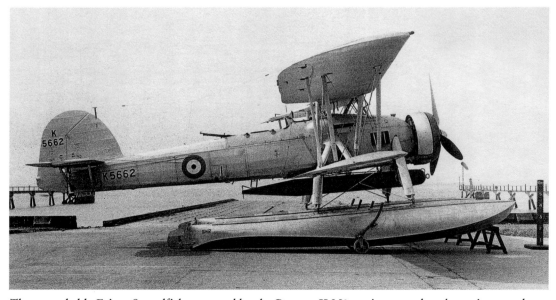

The remarkable Fairey Swordfish, powered by the Pegasus II M3 engine served as the main torpedo bomber of Fleet Air between 1936 and 1945. In spite of its outdated configuration it distinguished itself in many naval engagements. *DERA, Farnborough*

The RAE carburettor, side view. The air intakes and throttles are on the left. The upper linkages give servo assistance to the throttle controls. *DERA, Farnborough*

The RAE carburettor. This view shows the linkages between the boost (supercharger pressure) operated bellows inside the black cylinder nearest the camera, and the throttles visible at the top of the air intakes. The unit also compensates for air temperature and pressure changes. *DERA, Farnborough*

10869

The Bristol Hercules radial engine. It has fourteen cylinders in two rows of seven and precisely machined sleeve valves inside the air-cooled cylinders. It produced 1350 bhp in 1936 compared to 635 bhp from the Pegasus II M3 *DERA, Farnborough*

Five

Negative Gravity

The declaration of war did not immediately change the kind of work being done in Beatrice's section at Farnborough. Tests and development of the RAE carburettor and work on the prevention of icing were priorities as before. Before the end of 1939, however, the RAF had been in action against Germany, with bombing attacks on warships at sea and in harbour. Losses of Wellington, Whitley and Blenheim bombers were heavy, while Hurricane Squadrons stationed in France began to experience operational difficulties even before taking to the air.

On January 10th 1940, in Rouvres in Eastern France, the officer commanding 73 Squadron equipped with Hawker Hurricanes wrote in his Operational Record: "Difficulties experienced in starting engines in prevailing extremely cold weather, in a wind that extinguishes the Desmo starters." Later the same day the Squadron watched a Dornier 17 fly overhead, unable to intercept it, and as late as March 29th, an overnight frost produced the "usual trouble in starting up from cold." Other technical problems reported included a fatal crash attributed to failure of the pilot's oxygen supply and an unexplained engine cut at 22,000 feet.

Cold starting problems were also reported by United Kingdom-based squadrons in the bitter winter of 1939-1940 and Engine Department at the RAE applied itself to ways of improving the starting of engines at air temperatures down to and below -20°C. "Trouble shooting", initiated by reports from RAF units or requests from manufacturers through the Air Ministry, became an increasing part of the work of Farnborough.

In March 1940 German aircraft activity over France increased and RAF interceptions gave many pilots their first experience of combat. Then on May 10th, German forces burst into France, Belgium and the Netherlands, overwhelming opposition on the ground and in the air. 73 Squadron was forced to move away from Rouvres to Rheims, and then South to Gaye, constantly under assault from German artillery and aircraft. For them, as for other squadrons based in France or flying in from southern England, activity was constant and pilots were rapidly learning the strengths and weaknesses of their aircraft in combat with Messerschmitt Bf 109s and 110s. Defensive sorties were being flown continuously, often too many to be individually described in the Squadron's operational diary.

A serious problem which recurred in encounters with the enemy was misfiring and cutting out of the Rolls-Royce Merlin engine when a pilot pushed his Hurricane or Spitfire into a dive. Depending on steepness of the dive, this could range from a momentary splutter to several seconds without engine power: when pursuing or trying to escape from a Messerschmitt this was an unwelcome handicap. These engine cuts stemmed from the SU AVT/40 carburettors fitted as standard on Merlin engines. The cuts had been observed in early flight tests of the Spitfire in 1938, but until 1940 no one had anticipated the aerobatic nature of fighter battles. The RAF wanted urgent elimination of these misfires and the Ministry of Aircraft Production (MAP), looked for a solution to Rolls-Royce, the carburettor manufacturers and to the RAE – which meant Miss Shilling's Section.

German fighter aircraft did not suffer from similar engine cuts. Fuel flow was metered by a Bosch fuel injection system which delivered fuel directly into the cylinder, and it was uninterrupted by diving or inversion of the aircraft. Consequently they could dive with full power as soon as the stick was pushed forward. When air attacks on British airfields began in June 1940, intensifying in July with mass formations of German bombers and fighters, the Battle of Britain was under way, with no solution to Merlin engine cuts in sight.

Rolls-Royce and the RAE made concerted efforts to identify the cause. Beatrice and a small team, often working nineteen hour shifts at Farnborough, bench tested carburettors on a test rig, did mathematical calculations and set up flight testing to recreate the cuts and try out remedies. Meanwhile fighter pilots evolved their own ways of preventing the Merlin from stuttering: Air Commodore Peter Brothers CBE, DSO, DFC and Bar, then a Flight Lieutenant with 32 Squadron, recalls the manoeuvre that he adopted.

"I found the "negative G" (gravity) effect on my Hurricane a disadvantage on some occasions. For example, when an enemy fighter dived from behind, fired and carried on diving past, one could not immediately dive in pursuit without the engine temporarily cutting and causing one to be left far behind. This could be avoided by rolling upside down, pulling back on the stick into a dive (positive G) then rolling level in the dive, but whilst one had full power throughout, inevitably the aileron drag involved reduced the acceleration needed. Similarly, on sighting a target below, one suffered momentarily if one pushed the nose down to attack, a grave disadvantage."

Not every pilot liked this method: Wing Commander Bob Doe, DSO, DFC,

flying Spitfires from Middle Wallop from mid-August 1940, disliked turning upside down in flight, and when his engine cut out under negative g, he simply dived steeply to restart it with the propeller. His first experience of the problem was not when pushing into a dive but on flying into air turbulence caused by the slipstream of another aircraft – a German fighter that he was attacking from behind.

"I opened fire at about three hundred yards, and seemed to hit the one I was aiming at because he pulled up sharply. At that moment (I must have been down to about a hundred yards), I hit his slipstream and my engine cut – stone dead!"

Doe's Spitfire had dropped in the turbulence with the sudden lurch familiar to regular air travellers. The resulting negative g interrupted the flow of fuel to his engine just as the remaining Messerschmitts of his victim's flight appeared to see what was happening. Bob Doe was able to restart his engine in a dive and evade the group, shaken by his experience.

The term "negative g" (gravity) was not used in the first reports on the fuel feed problem, perhaps because the laws of inertia rather than of gravity were the real culprit. On June 24th, 1940, Engine Department of the RAE issued "Progress Statement No. 4: Cutting out of Merlin engines under high acceleration". Beatrice had ordered a series of tests on a Merlin-engined Battle aircraft at Farnborough which caused roughness and cutting out under a variety of conditions of fuel pressure setting and steepness of dive. Although the tests confirmed that downward acceleration produced fuel starvation, none of several remedies suggested, which included a remote electric fuel pump and modifying the altitude capsule, cured the cuts.

The search for a solution took almost a whole year, and even then provided only a partial cure, in Spring 1941. Complete elimination of the trouble took a further twelve months, by way of several false turns.

Looking back from the present, it seems surprising that it took so long to pin down the exact origin of the engine cuts. Investigations were complicated by other disturbances to fuel flow caused by engine vibration, such as frothing in the float chamber. It was not until December 21th, 1940, that the RAE delivered a firm and confident opinion in a Note entitled "Cutting out of engines under negative acceleration." It stated:

"Accelerometer tests on aircraft fitted with Merlin engines have shown that a cut may be expected to occur at negative accelerations greater than 0.9g. approximately . . . It is now conceded that this type of cut which is general on engines fitted with float type carburettors is due to loss of head causing fuel to leave the jet well at zero g (or, under the influence of engine vibration, slightly before this condition is reached)."

"Zero gravity" is the condition of weightlessness experienced when an aircraft changes from level flight to descending flight, or when it levels out from a rapid climb. "Negative g" follows as the aircraft starts to dive, at which point anything not fastened down, including fuel in the carburettor float chamber, surges upward. As the fuel outlet holes were at the bottom of the float chamber on the SU carburettors of Merlin engines, they were deprived of fuel and the engine coughed or cut out.

Identification of this "weak cut" led to several ideas for keeping the Merlin's carburettors supplied with fuel when subject to negative g. These included replacement of the float control of fuel intake by a diaphragm, designed by Cyril Lovesey at Rolls-Royce, and alternatively by a "negative enrichment valve" designed by AD Fisher of the RAE. What these suggestions failed to

recognise was that the "weak" cut was immediately followed by a longer and therefore more serious "rich" cut. The fuel that had been thrown to the top of the float chambers now forced the float to its lowest position, so opening the inlet needle valve. Fresh fuel rushed in below and then above the float at a pressure greater than the closing force provided by the floats, the fuel/air mixture becoming too rich to burn – hence the "rich" cut. Thus the engine fired again after the "weak" cut, only to be immediately choked by the following over-supply. This was why the engine was reported to "cut in and out" during diving tests of the Mk I Spitfire at Martlesham Heath in 1938.

It was Beatrice who worked out that the rate of delivery of fuel to the carburettors with the inlet needle valves wide open would prevent the floats from controlling these valves. She calculated the pressure and volume of fuel driven into the float chambers by the Rolls-Royce Merlin's dual fuel pumps, and devised a way of controlling this flow to allow only enough fuel for maximum engine power, but not enough to flood the float chamber. Her solution was a simple brass restrictor which was fitted between the end of the fuel intake pipe and the union at the entrance to the carburettor fuel inlet gallery.

This restrictor took the shape of a cone, then later on, a disc, with a sharp-edged hole of a prescribed diameter (See Appendix 1). It could be fitted to an engine while it was still in an aircraft at an operational airfield without removing the carburettor and it was promptly flight tested at Farnborough with satisfactory results. The restrictor was presented to Rolls-Royce and SU at a meeting at Rolls-Royce' Derby works in February 1941, by Beatrice and WC Clothier, who urged the two companies to do their own trials with the modification as soon as possible. The effectiveness of the restrictor in minimising the cut was confirmed, and the Royal Aircraft Establishment was instructed to go ahead with the manufacture and fitting of the first batch. These were made in the tool shop of the RAE, and Beatrice organised a small group from her section to go with her to Fighter Command airfields and show squadron technicians how to fit the restrictor. Beatrice was authorised to use her racing Norton, detuned for the road, for work, and her appearance at airfields with a bag of tools and a brisk manner became something of a legend. Thanks to Sir Stanley Hooker, the engineer who led supercharger development at Rolls-Royce at the time, the restrictor became known as "Miss Shilling's orifice" to pilots and fitters of the R.A.F. This probably amused her, recognising the language of familiarity rather than disrespect.

Beatrice was promoted to the grade of Senior Technical Officer on January 19th, 1941, becoming head of Engines and Accessories Section. Her staff were mainly young men trained in engineering, some at Technical College, some at University, some seconded from the RAF. She expected hard work, practical common sense and clarity of reporting from her team, no less when she was away travelling to the factories of aero-engine and carburettor manufacturers and the Ministry of Aircraft Production than when she was in Farnborough. When work continued into the night in her section, she would disappear briefly and return with fish and chips for everyone.

She was not gentle with those who failed to come up to her requirements. Summoned for "a word" to Miss Shilling's office, the offender would be fixed with a penetrating stare and asked in a barely audible voice to explain himself. The attempt to justify a failure, to observe a recommended procedure or to apply common sense, while Beatrice remained completely silent, was usually

punishment enough: she did not reprove in public.

But she was proud of her young men, and noted their later postings with approval. Two, Flight Lieutenants B Beeton and M Cox, became Principal Scientific Officers developing jet propulsion with Frank Whittle at the National Gas Turbine Establishment at Pyestock, near Farnborough. JEP Dunning became head of Rocket Propulsion Establishment at Westcott and AG Bowling became Engineer in charge of Aircraft Engine Servicing and Maintenance at Rolls-Royce.

For a year from early 1941 the fuel line restrictor reduced Merlin engine stoppages when diving to a hesitation or stutter, but it did not eliminate them altogether. As late as July 1941 the Wing Commander, II Group, Hornchurch noted of the new Mk V Spitfires: *"the 109 appears to have quicker initial acceleration in a dive and also in climbing. The greatest disadvantage in this respect is the cutting out of the Merlin engine on application of negative G."*

Engine Department was already working on a modified SU AVT/40 carburettor that would counter both the "weak" and the "rich" cuts. New shroud tubes surrounding the jet wells extended half-way up the float chamber, to a point high enough to draw fuel thrown upward by negative gravity, but still low enough to draw fuel from its "normal" place, i.e. in the lower half of of the chamber (See Appendix 1). The "rich" cut was eliminated by fitting new float needles which limited the maximum flow of fuel into the carburettor to the requirements of full engine power, as the fuel line restrictor or "orifice" had done before. Flight testing by Engine Flight of the RAE Experimental Flying Department enabled Beatrice to check and perfect her modifications. On March 31st, 1942, she wrote to Rolls-Royce, describing the innovations and asking for a standard SU AVT/40 to be sent to her "to incorporate our version of the modifications and let you have it by return."

The modified carburettor was approved by Rolls-Royce and ordered by the Ministry of Aircraft Production, and went into full-scale manufacture at SU (Skinner Union). There was little automation at SU in 1942, and assembly was on row upon row of little work benches by "the knife-and-fork method", as a wartime member of staff described it. Known as the "RAE anti-G carburettor", it was fitted to most Merlin engines between the XX and the 61. Its success earned Beatrice the respect of aircraft and aero-engine manufacturers as well as senior officials of the MAP. Her opinions were sought by their development departments, and she was obliged to travel regularly on overcrowded trains to Derby, Glasgow, Bristol and London, on rare occasions sharing a direct flight from the RAE at Farnborough. The new carburettor enabled full engine power to be called on in all combat situations, and gave Hurricane and Spitfire pilots new confidence in their aircrafts' capabilities.

Alex Henshaw, the gifted amateur racing airman and wartime Chief Test Pilot at the Castle Bromwich Spitfire factory, was one man who turned the negative g effect to advantage as part of his spectacular demonstration of the Spitfire's aerobatic abilities. He describes the final manoeuvre of his display in his book, Sigh for a Merlin.

"At the bottom of the inverted dive I would usually "round off" to a few feet above ground, and then I would push the machine into an almost vertical climb and, as it lost momentum from the negative "G" position, pull the control over gently to form a half-loop, hoping as I did so that the engine would burst into life as I opened the throttle. This it usually did with a spectacular sheet of flame pluming from the exhaust stubs caused by unused fuel that had accumulated during the inverted manoeuvres. With engine now on full power I would do a series of very low rolls left and right in front of the audience at hangar height, pull into a tight, fast engine-off turn and lower the flaps as I touched down for the landing."

The effect on his audience was stunned admiration.

The Rolls-Royce Merlin, a 27 litre V-12 cylinder engine whose power was increased from 1030 to over 2000 bhp between the Mk II and the 66. This is a Merlin III. The twin carburettors are at the bottom left, feeding the massive centrifugal supercharger.

Rolls-Royce Heritage Trust, Derby

"Somewhere in England", late in 1939. The first Spitfires to go into service were Mk I aircraft with wooden two blade propellers. They were fitted with Rolls-Royce Merlin II or III engines. *Science and Society Picture Library, London.*

Merlin XX and 21—A.V.T.40/193 Carburetter—Introduction of Fuel Restrictor Union to counteract Negative G conditions

MERLIN XX. LOG BOOK No. 26.	(MOD. NO. MERLIN/385.)
MERLIN 21. LOG BOOK No. 22.	(MOD. NO. S.U.853.)

(Class 2.)

(Research Engines 2898.—2.3.43.)

1. This modification introduces a restrictor orifice in the bore of the fuel inlet union of the carburettor to shorten the duration of the engine cut during the application of a negative acceleration in flight. It also prevents an engine cut during catapulting and serves as an interim but complete cure for instability of the float mechanism in carburettors of Serial Nos. 24101 to 28030, 5896, 5901, 5909 to 6254. (See A.P.1590G/D.5).

2. The undermentioned part is required to embody the modification and units are to submit demands as necessary to No. 16 Maintenance Unit, or the appropriate Royal Naval Store Depot, quoting this leaflet as the authority:—

For Merlin XX Engines:—

Stores Ref.	Part No.	Nomenclature.	No. off.	Class of Store.
36DD/55151	D19866 (or D.13280R or A.G.S.627FR)	Restrictor fuel inlet union	1	B

For Merlin 21 engines:—

Stores Ref.	Part No.	Nomenclature.	No. off.	Class of Store.
36DD/55276	D21701 (or D.13280S or A.G.S.627FS)	Restrictor fuel inlet union	I	B

3. The fitting of the restrictor union involves the replacement of the existing fuel inlet union (Stores Ref. 37C/61226) Part No. SU.04429 or (Stores Ref. 36DD/46336) Part No. D.13280. See Drg. No. A.P.1590G/D.7/43. After fitting the new union all joints must be fuel-tight and the union must be properly locked. Redundant unions of the original type and restrictor unions (see para. 4 (ii) below) are to be returned to No. 7 R.E.U. for subsequent return to the contractor for salvage purposes.

4. The following essential precautions are to be noted.

    (i) The fuel pressure at take-off power must not be less than 8 lb. per sq. in.

    (ii) A change in operational limitations may involve a change in restrictor. The restrictors are suitable up to a maximum of 12 lb. sq. in. boost R type and 16 lb. sq. in. boost S type at at 3000 r.p.m. Engines operating at above 12 lb. sq. in. boost (i.e., Merlin 21 engines only) must have the S type restrictor fitted.

5. In future spare carburettors will be delivered from the manufacturers without fuel inlet unions fitted. In the event of such a carburettor being received as a spare against demand the restrictor union (Stores Ref. 36DD/55151) Part No. D.19866 or (Stores Ref. 36DD/55276) Part No. D.21701, and joint washer (Stores Ref. 37C/61240) Part No. SU.04428 or (Stores Ref. 36DD/47600) Part No. A.57450, are to be transferred from the defective carburettor.

P.T.O.

L8070 TI/2 4/43 2500 C & P **Gp. 1**

The Ministry of Air Production modification order requiring the fitting of the anti-negative g restrictor to Merlin XX and 21 engines – in use by the Fleet Air Arm. The drawing of the restrictor and its fitting appear in Appendix 1, figure 3. *Public Record Office*

Efforts to improve cold starting and avoid
engine icing never ceased as aircraft flew at
higher and colder altitudes. This is an anti-ice
grill fitted to the carburettor intake of a Spitfire.

DERA, Farnborough

Parts from crashed German aircraft were studied at
Farnborough. This is a Mercedes Benz DB601 engine, an
inverted V-12 of 35.7 litres, from a Messserschmitt Bf 109
fighter aircraft. *DERA, Farnborough*

the corporal and the flight sergeant about Christmas leave and both say there is no chance whatsoever . . . I expect that you will want to hear some of the things I dislike about this life here, so I will give you some, they are mostly trivial in themselves but taken together they make a hellish life.

(a) We are not allowed to use the main stairs, we have to use the back stairs, which are narrow and ill-lit, in fact no lighting at all, you have to feel your way.

(b) We have seven beds in our room, maximum distance between beds six feet. I was up first immediately this morning and got the wash basin and started to shave. Two other blokes got up and without saying anything began to use the wash basin for shaving too . . .

(d) There are only three lavatories for the whole flight, one is in a bathroom, no toilet paper in two . . .

(g) March everywhere at 140 paces a minute (90 a minute is a comfortable rate.)

(h) Not allowed to use shelves for equipment, bed must be made up in the morning and all equipment placed on bed in prescribed positions . . .

(m) We were given no choice in rooms or room-mates . . . I do not like my present room- mates, they seem to be of low intelligence.

I think you had better approach Perring, say at the end of this week and tell him that I want him to get me back to the R.A.E. also tell him that if he won't do it I shall either apply for a technical commission or misbehave until I am thrown out."

George wrote an even more desperate letter two days later, urging Beatrice to tell Perring (WGA Perring, Deputy Director, Research and Experiment at the RAE) to get him out quickly, and asking her to reply by telegram. If there was a telegram, it did not contain the answer that George hoped for. George got his Christmas leave after all and Beatrice gave him her thoughts about his future in the RAF. After returning to "camp" at the Grand Hotel, Scarborough, George wrote home on January 2nd 1943:

"I caught my train at York all right, was in here by 6.31, what a waste with a pass to midnight. I have been feeling very queer mentally this week, last week I was acutely unhappy and fiercely resented every bit of discipline. Then last week you said I was to stay in the R.A.F. This week I have been dead mentally just as though I had a local anaesthetic in my brain, that isn't quite what I mean but it is the nearest I can get to a description in words . . ."

George ended a thoroughly miserable letter by saying that:

"One of the lads had made down my bed for me because they thought that I wouldn't be in until 12 p.m. and we have no light after 10.15 p.m."

Most people who join the armed forces undergo a period of basic training, in which they are subjected to seemingly mindless discipline, abuse, physical discomfort and more shouting than they will hear in the rest of their lifetime. The intensity of this experience can be traumatic, but whatever the merits or otherwise of this induction, it bonds its victims. George found that his room-mates not only made his bed for him when he was out late, but discovering that he was a slow mover, they gave him first place for washing in the morning "because they are amused at my slowness".

A request for shin-pads for football, and the modest admission that he got 100% in his morse exam were further signs of light in the darkness, though complaints were rarely missing from his letters while at Scarborough. A letter written on January 13th was, for George, almost upbeat:

"Scarborough, and 10 wing in particular, is as far as I can gather the worst I. T. W. (Initial Training Wing) for discipline and "bull" but the best for percentage successes. Which will be all to the good if I survive the course, though I don't appreciate it so much at the moment. Actually the life isn't too bad when you get used to it, by far the worst part about it is your absence . . .

The collars I took home are shrunk sufficiently so I will try to remember to have my photograph taken. I received the Angiers (and the cake) safely. It is unnecessary (at 14st. 4lb. Angiers is supposed to be for wasting diseases) but I am taking the stuff like a good boy . . .

Judging by the Russian's progress the war with Germany will be over by the time I have finished my training so I will be all set to return to Farnborough, I have no desire whatsoever to go to the Far East but I would like to have a crack at the Germans."

Initial Training would continue at Scarborough until late March 1943, with lectures on a range of technical subjects replacing more and more of the parades and polishing. George would not even start flying until summer, assuming he passed all his exams, and then a decision would be made as to the type of aircraft he was best suited to fly. He felt that Spitfires or Typhoons would be his kind of thing.

The De Havilland Tiger Moth II. It gave many pilots their first experience of flying and had a top speed of 100 mph. *DERA, Farnborough*

Airborn at last. George Naylor in the rear cockpit of a De Havilland Tiger Moth trainer at No. 10 Elementary Flying School, Fairoaks in May 1943. *Bryn Tennant*

Seven

Beatrice at War

Beatrice's domain at the RAE, 2AE Engine Department, was dominated by the carburettor test platform. This platform, fabricated from steel plate, measured about 20 by 30 feet and was mounted 8 feet high, above four large Nash "Hytor" vacuum pumps each one 6 feet in diameter. Their main function was to create altitude pressures for full-scale aero-engine testing in the nearby engine test house, but they also provided airflow and pressure to carburettors under test, so that air consumption and altitude could be simulated in any combination required. Suction and pressure were controlled by two large valves and fine-tuned by smaller bypass valves, and readings from different carburettor components were displayed on an instrument panel next to the valves. It was an important installation for efforts to increase engine power and overcome problems resulting from high altitudes.

During 1940 improvements in the engine power and aerodynamics of the Messerschmitt Bf 109 when it progressed from type E to type F left the Spitfire Mks I and II well behind in terms of speed and rate of climb. Rolls-Royce rose to the challenge by adapting from their new two stage supercharged Merlin XX power unit a simpler new engine which excelled at higher altitudes, and which could go straight into the Spitfire Mk I and Mk II airframe. The resulting Spitfire Mk V, with this more powerful Merlin 45 engine, was able to match the Messerschmitt 109°F.

But in September 1941 the Mk V proved to be unable to keep up with or get away from a new challenger, the Focke-Wulf Fw 190. Flight trials with an Fw 190 that had landed in South Wales (after a navigational error led the pilot to think he was over Cherbourg,) in June 1942, showed the German aircraft to be 20 to 25 mph faster than the Mk V at any altitude. The British aircraft which should have challenged the Fw 190, the Hawker Typhoon, went into Squadron service handicapped by serious problems with its Napier 24 cylinder engine and was unable to make use of its 400 mph performance until the worst of its problems were solved much later. So high were Fighter Command losses to the Fw 190 "Butcher Bird" that restrictions were placed on operations, while the Air Ministry and Rolls-Royce searched for a solution. Farnborough was also involved in the search. Work on dive brakes and controls was carried out by Structures and Mechanical Engineering Department and evaluated by RAE test pilots. A Mk V Spitfire was delivered to Farnborough for Engine Department to carry out trials of liquid oxygen injection to boost the power of its Merlin engine. The LOX system had been tested in flight in October 1941 and showed a 30mph increase in speed at 30,000 ft., and an impressive reduction in the time required to climb from 30,000 to 35,000 ft. However, as with other short cuts to increased power, new problems were created by the system, and fresh priorities pushed further development of LOX aside. Beatrice does not seem to have been directly involved in this project, but her team were working on improving engine performance by other means.

Like other departments, they were evaluating new equipment from North America. Until the bombing of Pearl

Harbour in December 1941, the United States was not at war with Germany or Japan. After Franklin Roosevelt was re-elected President for a third term in November 1940, however, he made no secret of his sympathy with Great Britain and he proclaimed the United States "the arsenal of democracy", with a duty to provide those "in the front line of democracy" with the weapons they needed. Britain was able to buy badly needed arms from America for dollars, and, when money ran out (which it did quite quickly), to receive them "free" from the "Lend Lease" arrangement a year before the U.S.A. declared war on Japan and Germany. The United States looked to long term benefits in return for their generosity.

One item that crossed the Atlantic with military hardware on convoys in 1941 was the Bendix Stromberg carburettor. This American instrument was of special interest to Beatrice because it was an injection carburettor, and as with the RAE carburettor on which she had done so much work, atomised fuel was injected directly into the supercharger, excluding any effects of negative g. Two versions were put through their paces on the test platform. Beatrice wrote a short report on the Bendix Stromberg after tests showed that the fuel mixture became excessively rich at high altitudes at high throttle settings, limiting engine power above 23,000 ft. She located the source of the problem at the altitude capsule which automatically adjusted fuel flow at varying air pressures, and proposed a modification that would give correct fuel mixture strength up to 31,000 ft.

She closed the report dismissively:

"It is concluded that the latest Bendix Stromberg injection carburettor is very little better than the one first supplied to this country in so far as the tendency to give unduly rich mixtures at altitude is concerned but that the very simple modification suggested by the RAE would give negligible changes in (fuel) mixture strength with altitude and would enable the carburettor to be used at greater altitudes."

By 1943 Bendix Stromberg carburettors, delivering correct mixture strengths at high altitudes, were fitted as standard to the Rolls-Royce Merlin engines being produced by the Packard company in the USA for British aircraft. Demand for this engine had became greater even than the greatly increased British capacity built up by Ernest Hives, the outstanding Director and General Works Manager of Rolls-Royce, could meet, so investigations into a suitable American partner were successfully undertaken. Packard produced 60,000 Merlin engines, which were fitted to Canadian-built Hurricanes and Mosquitos, and in yet greater numbers to the Mk III Lancaster.

Development and testing carried out by Beatrice and her team in their workshops were further tested in flight, whenever possible. The RAF appreciated the value of the Royal Aircraft Establishment's work and lent aircraft when they could be spared from operational flying, but usually several departments beside Engine Department had trials lined up and there was competition for flying time. Much of the flight testing of Beatrice's carburettor modifications to eliminate the negative g engine cuts had been done on the RAE's own Fairey Battles, light bombers from the 1930s withdrawn from service after suffering heavy losses in the Battle of France, and far slower than the Spitfires whose performance they were trying to simulate.

Beatrice was able to "borrow" more modern aircraft by 1943 and she went on test flights herself when she could. In August 1943 she flew with Bob Newton, who had joined her section as a 19-year-old trainee and was to work with her throughout the war, on a number of flights in Lancasters in pursuit of the cloud conditions which caused "icing up". Carburettor icing was a recurring problem on the long, high altitude flights between Bomber Command bases and their targets in Germany and Italy, sometimes with disastrous effects. On the night of September 7th-8th 1941, 71 aircraft flying to attack Berlin were recalled because of deteriorating weather. Twelve crashed on their return to England, because of either icing or poor visibility. On November 7th-8th, 1941, 37 aircraft were lost out of 392 sent to attack Berlin and Cologne. Many crashed into the North Sea after icing up of carburettors or wing surfaces in foul weather conditions of thick cloud, hail and storms. Beatrice and Newton wanted to subject the Bendix-Stromberg carburettors to this kind of cloud, thick and sleety, that produced icing, but could find none before Bomber Command wanted their Lancaster back.

The negative g effect continued to upset float carburettors not fitted with the full RAE modifications. In July, Beatrice mentioned in a letter to George:

"Newton had his first flight in a Mosquito with Cox doing lots of "g"s – This was most unofficial of course. He said he was not feeling so well after." Flight Lieutenant Cox had been seconded to Engine Department by the RAF and worked under Beatrice on the first negative g investigations. The same month, Beatrice was trying to arrange negative g trials with a Napier Sabre engine, and was planning to use the Mosquito again to test air cleaner modifications. In between she travelled regularly on trains which were carrying twice the passengers they had carried before 1940, on timetables frequently disrupted by air raid warnings, damage to the railways, and armed forces priorities.

There was not much to enjoy about these overcrowded journeys. Beatrice did not love children, but they seemed to find her interesting, and on one train insisted on blowing bubbles at her. Carriages were usually unheated, and the winters of

the 1940s were mainly very cold. Beatrice's destinations in 1943 were mostly the same as before: Rolls-Royce at Derby, Hucknall and Hillington in Glasgow; Bristol Engine Division at Patchway, Bristol; the S.U. Carburettor company in Birmingham; Napiers and the Ministry of Air Production in London. There were also more visits to operational squadrons, usually to "look at" problems thought to originate from carburettors. Cold starting, fuel systems and, increasingly, air cleaners for engine intakes were still the responsibility of the Section. If Beatrice was lucky, an aircraft from Farnborough might be flying to her destination.

In a letter sent to George on August 8th, 1943, Beatrice wrote;

"The position at work is very bad, I am sadly behind. The jobs aren't working in too well at the moment. I have 3 jobs I want flown and can't get them done without going and urging them myself. Still I'll finish some time."

Beatrice's Section issued twenty reports and thirty-eight technical notes in the years 1941-1943. She expected high standards of logic, and accuracy in her staff's writing and felt that too much needed checking and correcting before it could be passed on to the appropriate Director. It was a job she hated.

She was feeling the strain of hard work and long hours, not helped by an underlying belief that those at the top of the RAE were not doing all they could to ensure that the RAF had the full benefit of the Establishment's work as quickly as possible. She felt this strongly enough to tell the Deputy Director, Research and Experiment, WGA Perring, that if he was not going to make Headquarters in London take more notice of what was said at Farnborough, perhaps she and her colleagues could do more for the war effort elsewhere.

Beatrice smoked heavily, like many

others did at that time, and suffered from hacking coughs and regular stomach upsets. These were sometimes enough to keep her from work, and she would then try to catch up with home repairs and housework. Arriving home after a long day in Engine Department, her first actions were usually to brew a mug of tea, then to settle down to write to George. By then then the prospect of cooking can not have been inviting; she also complained to George of inability to get to sleep until very late at night. Not surprisingly, she sometimes complained to George of feeling "fed up" with work.

George, in his letters to Beatrice, complained about everything: lack of leave, lack of hot water, rudeness of his instructors, lack of letters from B, lack of clean handkerchiefs and lack of certainty that he would become a fighter pilot. Most of all, though, he complained of the absence of Beatrice, and after his regular assurances of love, his complaints must have had the effect of background noise on her. They also telephoned each other, and George suffered terribly from any nuance of tone that suggested criticism or displeasure. On August 17th, 1943, writing to Beatrice, he could not contain his unhappiness:

"Tuesday August 17, 1943

Hut 44, 29 E.F.T.S., Wolverhampton.

Beatrixie darling

I am worried, what was the matter with you tonight? I know that if we had been lucky we should have been together tonight and I should not be sitting up in bed writing to you now, I should be in bed with you instead. I am just as disappointed as you (probably more so because I have more spare time to think about it than you) but it didn't sound like that, it sounded as you used to be whenever you disapproved greatly of something I had done. I came away from the phone box feeling like a very chastened very young school boy, wondering what I had done

wrong. And I can't think of anything. I love you more and more as time goes on and I miss you more and more as the days go by and I don't see you. I am not going out with other women, I haven't even written to any of my girlfriends, at the dance on Sunday night I only danced twice and spent practically all the time talking to Nick. So what is it, darling, you are not jealous of my flying, are you, I know I fill all my letters to you with news of my flying but that is mainly because you ask for it . . . I don't like it when you sound so miserable, sweetheart, I know I was a bloody fool when I joined the RAF, but I thought you understood my feelings, they may have been cockeyed notions but I would have been a mighty poor lover if I wasn't willing to fight for you. Anyway darling, do cheer up, the war won't last much longer.

— All my love, George"

Beatrice answered:

"August 22, 1943.

Carfield, Ashley Road, Farnborough

George dear,

If you write me letters like the one just before you phoned me twice last week, I shall start catching the next train to Wolverhampton. Darling it is a shocking business this being separated. I do hope I see you on Tuesday. First they have the L.T.C. meetings the wrong way round i.e. R.R. on Thursday and Napiers on Tuesday and then they make it 9.30 a.m. on Tuesday and then the weather goes back on us. You are very unlucky on your solo weather.

I haven't seen you for 18 days, it is too long dear and between you and me I am going to make a job in Birmingham next week whether I see you or not this week.

You know dear that I am far too much in love with you to waste a 3 mins phone call being annoyed about you going to a dance or something. If I was with you for a day or so I would certainly find time to tell *you what I thought about you and your goings-on but I wouldn't waste much. Darling you know I love you very greatly, sufficient to encourage you in risking your neck in being a pilot or on a motorcycle more because I know you want to and will feel better if you are a pilot than because I want a pilot for a husband – you could become quite distinguished as a flutter – nark and stay a dart player for me.*

— All my love darling B"

There is nothing one can add to these letters to illustrate George and Beatrice's relationship more clearly. The term "flutter-nark" is a reference to George's work in Mechanical Test (later Structures) Department, before he left Farnborough to join the RAF

In May 1943 Allied troops, mainly American and British, completed the defeat of German and Italian armies in North Africa by capturing General Sixt von Arnim, the German Commander in Chief. In summer and autumn the Allies invaded southern Italy and started moving northward against fierce German resistance. In western and eastern Europe the German occupation stood fast, with elaborate and powerful coastal defences. Only bomber aircraft took the war into Germany, and Bomber Command now carried Britain's strongest hopes of defeating Germany. Production of aircraft and engines for Bomber Command was now the major industrial activity in Great Britain, and in 1943 the majority of aircraft produced were reliable four-engined machines capable of carrying large bomb loads at high altitudes. Raids on large German towns were made typically by forces of 300 to 760 aircraft, with occasional raids by over 1000 aircraft. The combination of Oboe target location and Pathfinder target marking with coloured flares brought accuracy of bombing undreamed of two years previously.

What had not changed was concern about the level of losses of bomber crews. In 1943 an average three out of every one hundred aircraft despatched on night bombing raids did not return. The proportion varied from one operation to another, but while one exceptional night may have brought no losses at all, others brought appalling tolls, and at the RAE there was always the thought – could they have been avoided? The nights of October 18th-19th and 20th-21st, 1943, were such nights: 34 Lancasters were lost on attacks on Hannover and Leipzig, the latter in bad weather conditions. Bad weather conditions with poor visibility led to in-air collisions and to wing and carburettor icing, even with carburettors heated for high altitude flying.

Beatrice wrote on 27th October:

"Tuesday the trouble I anticipate whenever I hear of bad weather and large losses caught up. It is most distressing as there is nothing we can do. We spent the day saying "but you can't do that because of so and so" or "that would take a year to develop and another year to produce."

She was not doing herself or her Section justice, because at this time another modification was being devised to the Bendix-Stromberg carburettor on Merlin engines fitted to Lancasters, which was to be tested in service in November. It was the kind of device that Beatrice and her team excelled in – simple and attachable to a standard component with a minimum of time and fuss. Known as "Tilly's Pepper Pot", it ensured that ice or snow would not cause a dangerous loss of pressure to the automatic mixture control. Beatrice was referred to as "Tilly" by her staff in her absence only. It was always "Miss Shilling", while she addressed even the longest serving members of her team strictly by their surnames.

George completed the theoretical part of his pilot training late in spring, 1943. He had been instructed in the theory of flight, airframe structure, engines, navigation and "signals" which covered communication by morse, Addis lamp and radio. He still felt that much time had been wasted during the five months, but took some pleasure in his high marks in the tests that were set in each subject. Now he was posted to ACDC Heaton Park, north of Manchester, to learn to fly.

Heaton Park was an Air Crew Dispersal Centre, which trainees shared with aircrew who had completed a tour of operations (in the case of Bomber crews in 1943 this was thirty completed bombing raids on enemy targets). These men were stationed here to wait for their next posting. Some stayed on at Heaton Park to train new aircrew. Others volunteered for a second tour of duty, a very brave decision for Bomber crewmen, given that less than half of all aircrew survived the thirty raids that made up one tour. George was billetted with a Mrs Stennet in Salford. The aircraft that served as trainer was the ubiquitous De Havilland "Tiger Moth" Primary Training Biplane, an open cockpit aircraft powered by the 130 bhp D. H. Gypsy-Major engine. At this stage all flying cadets, except for a very few transferred from other duties, held the rank of Aircraftman and had not been allocated to a specific branch or Command of the RAF. George still held high hopes of joining Fighter Command, though at thirty-one, he should have suspected that he was too old.

Many trainees and few aircraft led to a lot of waiting and little flying, a combination that was understandably unpopular; in three weeks George did twelve hours flying. But in three months he progressed from "circuits and bumps" – circuits of the airfield interspersed with frequent landings – to instrument flying, spins, stalls and basic aerobatics. He did not take naturally to flying and his first solo test, accompanied by an instructor to observe and, if necessary, save his life, was a disaster. A crowded airfield, a stiffish breeze and an impatient

instructor led to mistakes on the take-off, and the instructor took over the controls. One week later George tried again, with another awkward instructor. The take-off went well, then, George explained to Beatrice:

"I brought it in quite nicely but levelled out a little low. That would have been all right but when I have a test my brain slows down so I was slow in getting the stick back when we did settle down, so we bounced, it wasn't a bad bounce, but I had been told by Bladon to play it safe so I opened the throttle wide and went round again. Then the language started, Bladon cursed me fore and aft and sideways and from then on until the end of the test. Anyway the second one was a good three-pointer. Then he started to try to catch me out; twice he handed over to me when he had cut the throttle and we were outside gliding distance of the aerodrome so I had to use the throttle to get in (he wanted to see if I would try to land without throttle, undershoot and hit the hedge).".

After several more attempts to catch him out and a lot more swearing, the instructor surprised George by saying "Good show," and asking if he would like to fly unaccompanied. A successful solo flight followed.

George finished his elementary flying training at Wolverhampton Municipal Airport on September 29th, 1943. He scraped through the Chief Flying Instructor's test, but the CFI's report was less than enthusiastic.

FORCED LANDINGS:	Very poor
SIDESLIPPING:	Little Idea
POWER APPROACH:	Judgement poor
LANDING:	O.K. but rather rough
INSTRUMENT FLYING:	Fair
GENERAL FLYING:	Rather Overconfident

STYLE:	Poor
AIRMANSHIP:	Satisfactory
LOOK OUT:	Good
ASSESSMENT:	Just Average

"A keen pupil who is handicapped by a lack of natural aptitude. He is inclined to get nervous on test and at present his flying fails to inspire confidence. He always has an excuse ready."

George was quite philosophical about this report; he was placed 20th out of an intake of 31, and he received his posting to train at the Service Flying Training School at Cranwell College in Lincolnshire. Here he was impressed by the accommodation and facilities provided, but the board of senior officers who interviewed each arrival were adamant that he was too old for Fighter Command; he was to train on twin engined Airspeed Oxfords with a view to service in Coastal or Bomber Command.

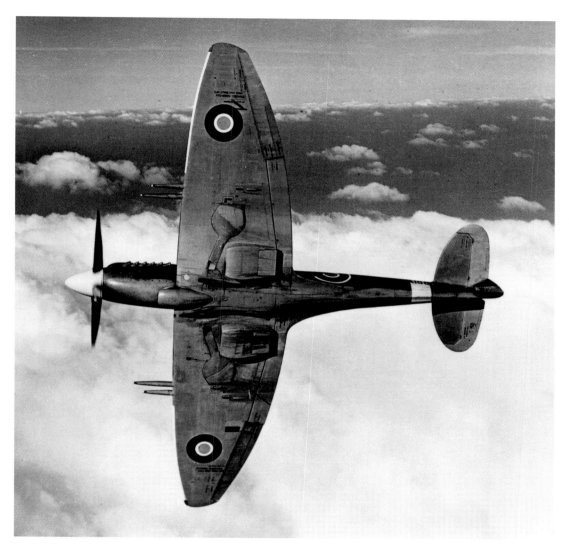

A Spitfire Mk V, hurried into production to meet the threat of new, faster German fighter aircraft in Winter and Spring 1940-41. Engine cuts on its Merlin 45 engine were much reduced by the first stage of Beatrice's work but not eliminated entirely until 1942. This Mk Vb is armed with four cannon in place of machine guns and was capable of 375 mph. *Royal Air Force Museum, Hendon*

The Focke-Wulf Fw 190 that landed at Pembrey near Swansea due to an error in navigation by its pilot on June 23, 1942. In Spring of 1941 the Fw 190 was faster than the Spitfire at all altitudes. The Pembrey Focke-Wulf was studied at the RAE and test-flown by the Air Fighting Development Unit at Duxford. *DERA, Farnborough*

A Hawker Tornado fitted on his own initiative by Roy Feddon of Bristol Engine Department with a Bristol Centaurus eighteen cylinder radial engine. With this engine the Tornado exceeded 400 mph in October 1941, making an unpopular point with Feddon's critics in the Air Ministry. Later Centaurus engines were fitted with the Hobson/RAE injection carburettor. *DERA, Farnborough*

The imposing 54 litre Bristol Centaurus engine at Farnborough for aircraft installation work. The early mark V Centaurus developed 2500 bhp; this rose to 3100 bhp in the latest versions. *DERA, Farnborough*

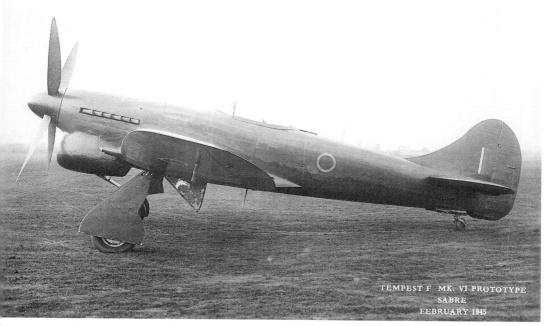

TEMPEST F MK. VI PROTOTYPE
SABRE
FEBRUARY 1945

The Hawker Tempest was one of the few aircraft to catch up and shoot down the VI flying bomb. It continued in service as the Tempest II with a Bristol Centaurus engine. *DERA, Farnborough*

Eight

The Home Front

On Boxing Day 1943, Beatrice wrote to George, now half way through his Service Flying Training at Cranwell. She had been riding with her sister's children, Janet, Marion and David.

"26.12.43

Dearest George

I bounced on my head yesterday and had a very bad ten minutes. I went riding with Nora's children (incidentally I am now finally and definitely decided that perpetuation of the race is a mistake) and I rode their pony which is a reasonable animal. It has no ambitions about moving fast but responds to the usually accepted noises, tugs at its head, kicks in the ribs etc. I was riding along with some of them in front and some behind when it dawned on me that I had fallen off, I didn't know where I was or what I was doing with these horses and children. Then instantly I wanted to know where George was, why wasn't he about, then I remembered George was in the RAF at Cranwell and he had been alright when he had caught the train at Grantham . . . I heaved a sigh of relief and investigated my own injuries."

These turned out to be bruising almost everywhere but no breaks or severe twists. The head troubled her for several days: "It is not quite stable on springing up from a recumbent position but I rarely do this and I expect another week will see the end of it." Beatrice did not see a doctor, and a few days later, after repairing and re-concreting a drain outside the house one cold evening, she felt so stiff and unwell that she prescribed herself two days off work. 1943 had been a hard year for Beatrice;

the fall was just the latest in a series of mishaps and short illnesses that assaulted her tough physique, while at work she still felt dissatisfied that her department had not done more to improve aircraft or save airmen's lives. On top of this, George's morale seemed to rest entirely on her comforting and encouragement.

Two events in 1943 brought light into life in Farnborough. Early in September American and British troops invaded the Italian mainland opposite Sicily, leading to Italy's surrender and the announcement of a military armistice against Germany on September 8th. Beatrice was able to surprise her staff with the news.

"The news came at a most appropriate moment. The Section was playing football with a ping-pong ball so instead of reprimanding them I was able to announce the red hot news and they forgot football and my lack of rebuke."

It looked as if the German army was really on the run after major defeats in North Africa and Russia earlier in the year. In fact it took another nine months of bitter fighting before the Allies clawed their way up Italy as far as Rome.

The second happy event in 1943 was the reappearance of Muriel Shephard, Beatrice's old friend and motorcycling companion in her student years in Manchester. Muriel had married Desmond Breed, the large, strong boyfriend who had been so helpful with push-starting racing motorcycles at Brooklands. Desmond, ten years Muriel's junior, joined the RAF at the beginning of the war and trained as a navigator in Bomber Command in Wales and Scotland, while Muriel worked in

Eastbourne. On his first bombing mission, on July 28th 1942, his Stirling was shot down, and Muriel thought that her conviction that he would not survive the war had been proved right. Desmond had not seen his daughter Elizabeth, "Biddy", born two months before he disappeared.

Then Muriel's house in Eastbourne was destroyed by bombing. In desperation she asked Beatrice if she would like a housekeeper and Beatrice welcomed her and her daughter to Carfield, her house on Ashley Road, Farnborough. The prospect of help with the house, and the possibility of arriving home after a demanding day at the Royal Aircraft Establishment to be served with at least a mug of tea must have been attractive. But Beatrice would have welcomed her in any case; she considered it normal to help anyone who needed it without fuss or ceremony, and Muriel was a friend with whom she had had much fun and many good arguments. The child was treated by Beatrice rather as a noisy little piece of furniture and was always referred to as "the infant". Beatrice professed to dislike small children and could not be seen to melt, but "the infant", now Biddy Fraser-Davies living in New Zealand, remembers being taken by Beatrice into bed to be comforted when Muriel, deafened by a bomb blast in Eastbourne, did not hear her baby screaming.

While the arrangement was vital to Muriel, it also helped Beatrice with more than housework, which was not Muriel's strongest point anyway. She was impulsive and imaginative and admired Beatrice greatly for her intelligence and achievements. This did not stop her from criticising her and offering suggestions for a better way of tackling problems of house maintenance or domestic planning. When her arguments failed to move Beatrice she would bet money that Beatrice's solution would not work, and Beatrice would accept – and usually win – the bet. They both

liked to read a good thriller and welcomed a stiff drink if one was offered. Although the infant disturbed Beatrice's sleep and ate the household jam ration, she and her mother distracted Beatrice from continuous thought of her work and George's problems, bringing some balance back to her life. Before 1943 ended Muriel had good news; Desmond was alive and well in a prison camp in Germany.

Work and George were linked by some of the engine and carburettor problems that occupied Beatrice's section, particularly after George moved on from training in the Airspeed "Oxford" to flying bomber aircraft at 30 Operational Training Unit at Hixon, near Stafford in April 1944. His last weeks at Cranwell had been most unhappy and disappointing. His plea to be considered for fighter training was firmly and finally refused, and he was told that his second choice, Coastal Command flying boats, was only open to Flight Lieutenants. George saw many of his coursemates listed for a commission, men whose marks in several of the final exams at Cranwell had been lower than his, while he remained a Leading Aircraftman. He was desperately keen on a commission, not only for the higher pay and status accorded to officers, but for the higher pension payable to his wife in the case of his death. He asked for an explanation from the Chief Flying Instructor and the Commanding Officer at Cranwell, both of whom hummed and hawed, and finally said that his flying was not good enough. This touched a raw nerve, as George knew that he was not an inspired pilot, but he had passed his flying tests, including night and formation flying, with average marks for his course. Nothing was to be done, in spite of George's energetic arguments, spoken and written at length to the CO. He was to join the ranks of bomber pilots needed to execute the strategic plans of Air Marshal Harris. At the end of his course at Cranwell, George was awarded his pilot's wings and was promoted to the rank of Sergeant. Next stage was a move to the Operational Training Unit at Hixon.

Two days after arriving at the Operational Training Unit, the newly posted pilots were told that they had four days to get their aircrew together. With no more guidance than an initial denoting each man's training on his chest, N for Navigator, O for Radio Operator, B for Bomb-aimer to guide him, pilots had to choose in ignorance of character and past experience and hope for the best. It was probably as good a way as any, considering the unimaginable circumstances they might have to contend with, and it made the pilot the creator as well as leader of his crew. George wrote late on the first day for selection:

"I have a crew, it's been a bit of a gamble getting them. We were told this morning that we have to be crewed-up by Monday, it is the pilot's choice but in my case 4 out of the 5 asked me first if I would take them. It's a bit stupid because we separate for lectures (pilots together, etc.) and so we have no real chance to know one another, in fact I wouldn't be certain with most of them whether they belonged to our course or a previous one. By lunch most of the pilots were in a flap though one or two had complete crews, I of course had no-one. That was about 1.30 p.m. by 2.55 p.m. I had my complete crew, namely:

Navigator – P/O Joiner – Scotch

Bomber – Sgt. Bearden – Australian

Wireless Op./ A.G. – Sgt. French – Australian

A.G. (Probably Mid-upper) – Sgt. Jaye – British

A.G. (Tail Gunner) – Sgt. Lavender – Welsh.

It is fairly certain that we are going on to conversion course to 4-engine bombers and highly probable that it will be Lancasters."

George was to train on twin-engined Wellington bombers, by now replaced in active service over Germany by four-engined aircraft which were faster, more heavily armed and less prone to crash if an engine failed. The Wellingtons mainly used at OTU were aircraft that had seen service in bomber squadrons and been used operationally, hence were quite worn and "usually rattled somewhat" according to a former fellow pilot. There was also a stiff programme of lectures and practice drills, some of which, such as practice with oxygen masks in the decompression chamber, were done together by the new aircrews. Before flying a Wellington George had to find and learn all its instruments and controls, and to learn the basics of his crew's jobs beside his own. An unpleasant surprise was to find that starting the engines was a job shared by the pilot and a ground crewman, who had to climb up to the engine nacelle to operate the priming pump after turning its fuel cock on. He then had to climb around the engine nacelle to turn off the priming cock and then down to the ground in a gale created by the now speeding propeller. George did not enjoy doing this, a routine developed by Beatrice's section early in the war, and he told her that she should work out a way for one of the aircrew to prime the engines while inside the aircraft.

On May 12th George did a two-hour flight:

"Started off by throwing it round the sky (heaving and pushing, I did stick turns and dives, it takes practically all my strength with both hands on the wheel to pull it out of a dive). I don't like Wellingtons, the controls are far too heavy, you can't "feel" the controls you just put all your weight on to them, my shoulders are still tired. The worst part about them though is an automatic trimming gear when the flaps go down, this means that the aircraft is left tail-heavy and cannot be trimmed for the final approach. An

excellent idea for killing people, it means that you have to create a considerable forward force on the wheel, if you slow at all the nose comes up and the speed falls off very quickly; it is absolutely asking for people to stall on the approach."

Beatrice was anxious that George should grasp the correct order of use of the several fuel tanks of the Wellington, as air locks and stalled engines could follow using the wrong sequence. She also tried to clear up a difference of opinion between George and his engine instructor regarding use of the two speed superchargers on the Wellington III's Bristol Hercules engines. George disagreed that engine damage would result from changing from low to high supercharger speed while climbing under full or near-full power, and that waiting for engine speed to drop before changing while climbing after take off was not necessary. Beatrice gave her opinion with a clarity that can be appreciated by those who are lost in the world of superchargers and boost. ("Boost" is the pressure to which the supercharger compresses the air-fuel mixture delivered to the engine at a given moment.)

"You are 100% right about the gear change. The boost control is quite capable of dealing with very rapid changes of boost. The loss in power on changing to high gear from low is appreciable and with an overloaded bomber makes a big difference in the climb. The surge more noticeable in Merlins than Hercules is often attributed to the supercharger but there is no definite evidence that this is so and I attribute it to carburation (fluctuating fuel feed pressures and altitude) and sometimes it is traced to the boost control or the propeller. If you get a pukka boost surge you won't be in any doubt about it – both boost and r.p.m. go completely haywire on the testbed. A prop will of course with its greater inertia restrain it a bit but I think it would be worrying in the air . . . The engines you are on now (Merlin and Hercules) are

rated far nearer their limits than the Cheetah (engine on the Oxford trainer) and it does not pay to exceed cylinder temperatures etc. On the Hercules a short period of high cylinder temperatures may lead to gummed junk head rings and piston failure."

The danger of engine failure or stoppage in flight through negligence was brought home to Beatrice after a visit to Plymouth to fly in a Coastal Command Sunderland flying boat piloted by the Australian Group Captain commanding the station. The first flight was cut short by the appearance of an unidentified aircraft; the Sunderland had no guns and weaved through the balloon barrage to set down quickly. As the problem she was investigating was poor starting and slow running of the aircraft's Bristol Pegasus radial engines, Beatrice checked the carburettors and went over the starting up procedure with the fitters who serviced the aircraft, in particular priming the engine, and then left them to set the slow running. There was time for a short flight before dusk during which one engine spluttered, cut out but then picked up again. Next morning the Sunderland started easily but Beatrice thought the pilot was over-revving and climbed in to tell him so. He complained that the engine had run away with him, and investigation showed that the throttle had become disconnected because the fitters had gone off to another job without locking it. So it had been unlocked throughout the flight the previous evening, when a runaway engine would have at the least made landing very difficult."The Group Captain was shaken," Beatrice reported.

At the same time that George started flying Wellingtons, a number of mysterious engine cuts on this aircraft were reported to RAE, usually when the pilot was about to change from take-off power to climbing power. The cuts occurred only on Wellingtons, although Halifax and Lancaster MkIIs used the same engine without similar problems. A Group Captain from 91 group, Bomber Command, met with Beatrice and one of her staff to discuss possible causes and concluded that something about the installation of the engines on the Wellington caused the problem; Beatrice suspected some interaction between the hydraulics that raised the wheels after take-off and opened and closed the bomb doors, and the functioning of the carburettor. She warned George to learn to land on one engine, and promised to base an investigation on his unit at Hixon if more cuts were reported. Meanwhile she drove up to Bristol Aero Engines with a colleague to carry out trials to locate the source of trouble. She described the three-and-half hour journey in an elderly Vauxhall, whose engine had just two cylinders working when they reached Bristol, but about the trials said only that she had managed to set a Hercules engine on fire.

Home life in Farnborough at the end of May 1944, had swung from the solitary existence of the winter of 1942-3 to a surplus of residents. "It is a sad thing but I can't call my house my own at the moment." Beside Muriel and her daughter, another old friend, "Bunty" Annis, who had partnered her husband in a transport business and herself drove 60-foot Scammel aircraft transporters, was staying as a self-invited guest while deciding what to do about a job after her marriage and the transport business disintegrated. There was also Rita, Beatrice's new retriever pup and great friend of little Biddy, sharing each other's food when adults were not watching. One of Beatrice's colleagues was greatly attracted to Bunty and visited too often for Beatrice's liking, but as Bunty was an old friend she tolerated these visits up to the point when they tried to disappear into the bedroom together.

The regular residents at Carfield had well-defined duties: Beatrice paid the

bills, repaired the plumbing, electrical faults and any broken pens, tools or cigarette lighters, and gave out orders; Muriel planted and cared for the fruit and vegetable garden, cooked supper and tried to clear both the supper dishes and the infant out of sight by 7.30 pm, and Rita the pup was responsible for waking Beatrice in time for a morning walk and a punctual start at the RAE. Rita was unreliable in carrying out this duty, and Beatrice often started and finished late at work.

She also brought home work involving calculations and analysis of tests, and was absolutely furious when deductions were made from her salary for days lost through uncertified illness in 1943. She addressed the Deputy Director of Research, Engineering:

"I have worked a greater number of hours than the number of hours in a full working year (no leave) with the present hours of attendance, and I believe that I am entitled to 36 days leave with pay."

As usual, Personnel Department was not prepared to deviate from a decision once it was made, and Beatrice told George that she would leave the RAE to start an independent engineering concern with him as soon as the war was over.

She longed to be creating fast cars and motorcycles from the unused sporting machinery that was sitting out the war, working with George and doubtless firing sardonic comments on the standard of his workmanship at him, as she had done at Brooklands. George too looked forward to racing motorcycles again, and wrote that he was sure that he could take the class lap record at Brooklands with the supercharged Norton if Beatrice would just let him keep "flat out". He did not know that Brooklands no longer existed as a race track as large sections had been blown up to prevent German aircraft from using it as a marker for raids on London, and to extend a runway for the Vickers aircraft factory. They looked out for likely cars for rebuilding for racing, and Beatrice took a particular fancy to the Lagonda "Rapier", a sporting saloon powered by an engine with great potential for tuning.

On May 27th Beatrice warned George that rail services had been cut drastically, and travel would be difficult. Massive movements of American and British troops and the exclusion of the public from much of the south coast made it obvious that an Allied landing in France was about to take place, and on June 6th this invasion, "D-Day", began. Over 1000 aircraft of Bomber Command battered the Normandy coast the night before "D-Day", and 1300 bombers of the US Eighth Army Air Force continued the attack on German defences in daylight as the invasion fleet approached France.

George was now well advanced in handling the Wellington Bomber, and he absorbed the complexities of navigation and flying by instruments without difficulty. He seemed to have a gift for locating himself in good and bad visibility. The next stage was the Heavy Bomber Conversion Unit at Sandtoft, to fly Halifax Vs with Rolls-Royce Merlin engines. He knew these engines well from Beatrice's work when he had been at the Royal Aircraft Establishment, and was shocked to hear the Engineering Officer say at a lecture on the Merlin engine that all the anti-negative g bits had been designed by a girl in the Rolls-Royce drawing office.

"That was more than I could stand, I informed him coldly that the design had been done by a Miss Shilling of the RAE. When he had recovered he said that that was what they were told when they went on the engineering course at Rolls. I think it is a bit too thick. Rolls make an absolute mess of the whole job and then claim the credit when you do it properly."

If Beatrice was put out, she did not say

so. Her next letter was written after an alcoholic meal celebrating a friend's return from the United States. *"Just to show how tight I am – 4 double whiskeys and some beer, plus a five shilling brandy. Anyway I have ridden a push bike home more or less straight."* Bunty added her P.S. *"George dear, Your wife is highly drunk and incapable, and for that matter so am I. Lets hope that we recover sufficiently by Thursday, because to deal with you, one MUST have one's facilities and capabilities in action"*. George was due home on leave next Thursday.

After he got back to his unit from leave, he flew the Halifax under instruction, in daylight and at night. On his first night flight the instructor was nervous and on landing George found that he was wrestling his set of controls while the instructor was gripping the second set and aiming at a different part of the runway. They landed safely, fortunately, as the Halifax could cause trouble for an inexperienced pilot. George still found the Halifax more pleasant to fly than the Wellington and easier to trim, or keep in the best position or "attitude," for level flight and landing. Before the end of August 1944 George's commission as Pilot Officer finally came through, to the relief of George and the delight of his family in Yorkshire and Farnborough.

After six weeks there was only one stage of training left, the nicely titled "Lancaster Finishing School". For George this was a two week course at No.1 L.F.S. at Hemswell, near Gainsborough in Lincolnshire, where he was to fly and learn the characteristics of the Lancaster bomber. This was an aircraft of towering size, compared to other bombers of the Royal Air Force. It weighed thirty tons when laden with 12,000 lb of bombs and those flown by George were all powered by four Merlin engines. They had agility and performance surprising in such a large aircraft, withstood hefty stresses in rapid turns and high speed in dives, often at well above the maximum dive speed recommended of 360 mph. It earned a reputation as a strong and vice-free machine.

George was not an immediate enthusiast, however:

"I think the Lancaster will be easier to fly than the Halifax in everything but landing. But I am not so hysterical about it as the other pupils. The Halifax is classed as a bad aeroplane because with flaps and undercarriage down it needs a hell of a lot of power to fly straight and level but this means that when you do sit her down a bit hard she stays down whereas a Lanc will balloon sky high (a ground instructor pilot told us of a bloke coming back in bad weather when the cloud base was 150 feet who bounced back into the cloud on his first attempt to land.) . . . The priming pump on the Lanc is in a stupid place, I don't blame the ground crew for not priming while turning the engines to start. The hydraulic system on the Lanc is such that if you select undercarriage UP with the engines stopped nothing will happen, if the engines are started the hydraulic pumps work and the undercarriage will collapse, anybody priming engine at that point stands an excellent chance of being squashed flat."

In fact, a landing violent enough to produce a 150 feet bounce would collapse the undercarriage of a Lancaster, so the story of "ballooning" was the product of someone's lively imagination. George came to respect the stability and handling of the aircraft. He later had to make three emergency landings with Lancasters, one with a full bomb load, without damage to the aircraft or any crew members.

Beatrice hoped that he would never fly one in action. The Russians were advancing on Berlin at a rate of ten miles a day in August 1944 and had about 325 miles to go half way through the month. They could be there before George had time to settle into his operational squadron if they kept up this rate through September, but of course they did not, and fought ferociously to reach the shattered city late in April 1945. Meanwhile Beatrice did her utmost to warn George of the technical hazards that could face him even on an aircraft as well designed and tested as the Lancaster. About overspeeding of the propellers, which could lead to the destruction of an engine through over-revving she wrote:

"At slightly odd attitudes the feathering oil in the tanks is not properly trapped. (outlet to feathering pump uncovered.) The valves in the constant speed unit have stuck open in some cases and the pressure been lost. If one does overspeed reduce the aircraft speed and altitude to get the r.p.m. down to a minimum. Moral – be sure you can find the feathering button in the dark without any hesitation as things happen quickly i.e. 5 secs."

She also warned of another kind of hazard, which she heard about from Jock West, ex-motorcycle racer now a Wing Commander with an engineering command. A Tempest pilot flying above thick cloud received radio instructions to steer South on 135 degrees, to a named aerodrome, to which he would be guided. After a while he felt uneasy and dived down to find himself over the Channel. A German station had tried to get him to land in occupied France. It was a female speaking "The siren" – as West said.

Many members of staff at Farnborough did dangerous work. Dorothy Robson, a specialist in bombsight development, calibrated these on flight test. She was killed in November 1943 when the Halifax V bomber she was flying in crashed on high ground in Yorkshire. She was only 23, one of the "rookies" among the scientists at Farnborough. *Brenda Rimmer*

The Wellington bomber. George began Operational Training on Wellingtons in March 1944. He did not get on well with them. *DERA, Farnborough*

George was much happier once he received his commission and was posted to the Lancaster Finishing School, the last stage of his training. *Anne and Dennis Lock*

The four engined Halifax with Merlin XX engines, a type that George enjoyed flying at the Heavy Bomber Conversion Unit at Sandtoft. *DERA, Farnborough*

Nine

George at War

In summer 1944, Beatrice was in more danger at home in Farnborough than George was while learning to fly Wellington bombers at Hixon. In the middle of June, a week after D-day, an assault was launched on London by flying bombs from German sites in northern France. Over 2400 were launched before the end of the month, and although they were well-aimed and their design included an automatic engine cut-out intended to land them on or near Tower Bridge, half of the bombs that reached the English coast landed on the southern and south eastern counties. On June 17th Beatrice told George: *"One of the pilotless planes must have landed on Godalming. Thursday night was one damn siren after another."*

The rate of launches, averaging around 150 every 24 hours, was tiny compared to the weight of bombs dropped each night by Bomber Command on German cities and flying bomb launch sites in the same period. Beatrice was not worried: *"If they send 100 over each night it will have a good nuisance value but only that, because the scatter must be pretty wide and a lot will land in open fields."* For an uninformed guess, this was an surprisingly accurate summary of the true situation, though few people shared her cool assessment of the danger. Only two thirds of the bombs launched reached England, and half of those crashed in fields after being shot down or because of mechanical failure. Nevertheless, those that hit housing or cities caused massive damage and many deaths. Over 6000 people were killed by flying bombs, and most Londoners were very afraid of them. The bombs were known to the Germans as "Vergeltungswaffe 1" (Reprisal Weapon), or V1.

Visiting London with GJ Armstrong, her immediate superior in Engine Department, for a week of planning and discussions at the Ministry of Air Production, Beatrice stayed with the Armstrong family in south London:

"His wife was feeling jittery because they've had 18 fly bombs within audible and some within visible range. A flying bomb came over while I was there. The engine stopped and within five seconds "wop" she went. I comforted Mrs Armstrong as much as possible but to a non mechanically minded person with a young kid, hearing the things, wondering whether it is coming towards you and waiting for the engine to stop must be a bit unnerving."

Beatrice's mother wrote to her from Godalming with her own bomb story:

"Dearest B,

We had quite an alarming time yesterday morning (8 a.m.) I was looking out the door and saw a Doodle Bug flying across the sky; it then began to squeal or whistle and I realised what it was – I turned in and there was a terrific bang. It fell just at the top of Holloway Hill in the garden belonging to a big house, wrecking that and several others, it stripped the trees of their leaves felling others – broke many shop windows in the town – two windows in the house next door – Mrs. Roberts and I felt very shaky for some time but all that happened in our house was the key fell out of the pantry door and two medicine bottles came down from the shelf neither of them breaking. Across the road it blew two eggs off the table on to the floor – they were not so lucky as not to break."

The first V1s proved very difficult to intercept, and not knowing how many of them might come over the Channel, the Government, including Churchill, were extremely worried. Newspaper reports of "Terror Weapons" did not help public morale and over a million people, mostly children, were evacuated from London before the end of July. A Flying Bomb Sub-Committee was formed by the Air Ministry to recommend "improved technical countermeasures".

The sub-committee met weekly from June 26th 1944 and discussed a range of possible measures. These included; anti-aircraft fire (although it was felt that at around 3000 ft the bombs flew too low for Heavy AA fire and too high for Light AA. fire); shredded paper released by rockets or parachutes to clog the V1s' engines; water, methanol or nitrous oxide injection to speed up the fastest fighter aircraft available; a wider spread of barrage balloons, and assaults on German V1 bases. Bomber Command was already attacking launching sites in France. The committee focussed on boosting the performance of fighter aircraft. It was stated that the Napier Sabre and Rolls-Royce Griffon engines would not withstand more than the maximum boost already supplied by their superchargers, but that work on the Merlin engines on the American Mustangs being flown by Fighter Command might be worthwhile. These were the Packard-built V1650 Merlins with Bendix-Stromberg carburettors.

The Committee did not add any practical measures to those already in use by the armed services. Two interesting points emerge from the Committee's meetings. From the suggestion of clogging the V1s' engines, it is clear that it was already known within two weeks of the first launch that they were powered by a jet-type engine with an air intake, not rockets, and secondly, although there was a widespread belief

that some fearless fighter pilots had caused V1s to crash by flying alongside and "toppling" them by touching wings, the Committee were unable to find a single pilot who had done this. After the Committee ceased meeting, however, on August 4th 1944 a Gloster Meteor pilot, Flying Officer Dean, flew alongside a V1 after his guns jammed and tipped it over into a crash dive by lifting his wingtip after manoeuvring it under that of the German missile.

Beatrice and Fighter Command believed that there was just one sure way of stopping V1s – to intercept them and shoot them down before they reached the outskirts of London. There was no question of lengthy development of new engines or sophisticated modifications to superchargers. The threat from V1s was immediate and alarming, though it was not until late July that the RAE gave Beatrice the responsibility for devising a power boost to enable Mustangs to catch up with the V1 quickly enough to intercept them. On August 8th she wrote to George:

"We're trying to get extra fuel (alcohol) through a carb and have it ready for fitting to an aircraft at 8 a.m. tomorrow. Needless to say it is 11.00 p.m. and some silly bloke has switched everything off because I took the troops out for some beer at 9.45 p.m."

Bob Newton, working in Beatrice's Department, describes this work, in which he had a major part:

"Rather than trying to raise the boost on 100 octane alone, it was decided to get the extra power required from alcohol, not by direct injection into the inlet manifolds, which would have needed considerable development, but by using a spray bar (simply a shaped copper tube) in the air intake. B [Beatrice] got this job and unloaded the mechanics of it onto me.

"Since the stoichiometric air/fuel ratio for methyl alcohol (otherwise known as methanol) is about 7 to 1 compared to 14

to 1 for petrol, the carburettor must be retuned to provide the correct mixture strength (in this case at maximum power) according to the ratio of petrol to methanol chosen. I did this using the carburettor taken from a Mustang which we had at RAE and which was later to be flight tested with the modded carb refitted. As for all such modifications of complete carbs, the tests were done on the carburettor test platform, tweaking the settings at simulated altitudes similar to those mainly used by the V1s. This was done so that the change to methanol could be selected by the pilot simply by pressing a button.

"B and I then took this modded carb up to the Rolls-Royce test bed facility at East Kilbride near Glasgow, where it was fitted to a 60 series Merlin and run up to combat power prior to switching on the alcohol. This engine had been fitted with stub exhaust pipes so that one could see the change in colour of the gas when the methanol was switched on. B and the RR personnel stayed in the control room watching the instruments to see what was happening whilst I went into the test cell (by choice!) to get a close look up the stubs for the same purpose.

"The noise from a Merlin under those conditions and in a closed cell was an experience that I shall never forget; it is almost as if it was yesterday. Due to the vibration, it felt like one was standing 2" above the floor which consisted of the usual steel plates. The heat from the exhaust gasses (the stubs were approaching white heat) as one looked up the bank of six outlets from a crouched position about three feet away was like looking into mini-hells and one's ears were approaching the threshold of pain. I could actually see into the combustion chambers past the exhaust valve heads which, of course, were red hot and appeared to be hovering stationary above their seats. But I wouldn't have missed it for anything.

"When the controller saw from the instruments that the engine was stabilised at full power, he signalled to me through the observation window and, when I was concentrating fully on the gasses I gave him the thumbs up to switch on the alcohol. Sure enough, the colours changed from the normal mix of red white and blue to include a dull yellow and, although I don't know how, I sensed that the power had indeed increased. I wasn't wrong.

"A few seconds later I glanced at the window and saw a look of horror on the controller's face. Then there was a very loud bang and I instinctively dived into the corner of the cell. During this very short journey I became aware that apart from a hissing sound all had gone quiet and people were coming through the control room door into the cell. After assuring them that I wasn't hurt at all, I picked myself up and looked at the engine which was a sorry sight. The hissing noise was from the glycol coolant which, still under pressure, was spurting out of one of the front coolant jackets and there was oil all over the place together with a lot of bits of aluminium. But none of it hit me.

"All of this, of course happened a lot more quickly than it takes to tell but my abiding memory is watching number one connecting rod, minus its piston and a bit bent, swinging gently upside down beneath the broken crankcase. During the subsequent account of all this, it emerged that the look of horror on Dennis Bickerton's face – he was the Rolls-Royce controller – appeared when he discovered that, due to the sudden surge of power, the Heenan and Froude brake failed to operate fast enough to absorb it (the extra power) so consequently the engine revs which were already at 3000, went off the clock."

Somehow, Beatrice persuaded Rolls-Royce to provide another engine, although the test bed was needed seven days a week to test-run production engines up to full power. After test bed staff had spent the night clearing up and connecting a fresh engine up to the test brake, a new start was made the next morning. Once more the Merlin was brought up to maximum power; the methanol injection was started and this time the engine power increased without over-revving. Bob Newton, again in his precarious crouch near the stub exhausts, suddenly noticed the top of the cylinder liner drop and as coolant flowed through the gap that resulted, he signalled frantically to the controller, who was able to shut the engine down before it was badly damaged. This was enough for Beatrice, Bob Newton and Rolls-Royce, who had given their best help to a project about which they had misgivings.

Back in Farnborough with the modified carburettor, Beatrice ordered one last attempt to make the "quick-fit" methanol injector work. The carb was refitted to its Mustang, Bob Newton obediently started up the engine, held his breath and pressed the methanol button. The engine ran on the mixture – very hot – but it ran. To Bob's great surprise an RAE test pilot, Squadron leader Moffat, agreed to take the aircraft up and try the modification. He flew, returned, and in response to Bob's question, "How was it?", said "If you want that thing flown again, you can (unprintable expletive) well find someone else." Apparently on turning on the alcohol the engine vibrated so badly that he could not read the instruments and was afraid the engine would tear itself from the airframe.

Beatrice was disappointed, but accepted defeat. She and Bob had worked hard and hopefully on this project although past experience had shown that few aero-engines liked to be pushed beyond their design maximum revs and boost. In any case, by September improvements in the reliability of the Hawker Tempest's Napier engine changed it into a formidable V1-chaser, and Tempest squadrons claimed 638 flying bombs destroyed. The new Gloster Meteor jet aircraft destroyed another 13 V1s in its first week of service flying with 616

Squadron in Summer 1944, and the Mk XIV Spitfire, with 2000 horsepower of Rolls-Royce Griffon engine power, also caught and shot down a number of V1s. Anti-Aircraft gunnery from the ground also developed to meet the threat more effectively and by mid-September, attacks by V1s had all but stopped. Over 8600 had been launched at Britain.

Just before her visit to Rolls-Royce in Glasgow, Beatrice was promoted to Principal Technical Officer. In a letter congratulating her on her promotion, the Director of the Royal Aircraft Establishment, WS Farren, wrote:

"I have long admired your outstanding contribution to the R.A.E.'s efforts to make itself felt in the Engine world. I trust that this encouragement will stimulate you to carry on with the good work.

I think the prospects before the Power Plant Division are good. Everyone recognises that we have to build up again, but I believe that we have a good foundation on which to start, and, with energy and enterprise, we can now do what should have been done long ago.

As you know, promotion to Principal may be on the score of personal achievement, or on the score of administrative responsibility, or, most usually, on both. In any event it marks the individual as a potential leader and inspirer of others. I know that the Head of your Division has confidence in you, and I can assure you that I have.

P.S. There is a small personal matter on which you can help me. Would you come and see me some time soon?"

This promotion came soon after Engine Department was reorganised into a new "Power Plant Division", a reorganisation which, inspired by the success of Frank Whittle's work and the effectiveness of the Gloster Meteor jet aircraft, anticipated an end to piston engine work at the RAE. Beatrice described to George a confusing re-shuffle of duties, in which two people appeared to have responsibility for carburettors and superchargers, and her former colleague, GJ Armstrong, became Head of Power Plant Division and Gas Dynamics Department. She acquired the title "Experimental Supervisor", in charge of flight tests and most engine testing, but was not happy at the thought of checking and correcting the reports of technical officers whose grasp of logic and mathematics was poor by her standards.

The intriguing reference to "a small personal matter" in the Director's letter was that he had got the Senior Mess at the RAE finally to agree to admit women, but no women would apply for membership as they thought they were not wanted! Farren hoped that Beatrice would not be so reticent, and she readily supported him by applying for membership, although she was not really interested in the issue. She felt she was working harder and more effectively than most men at the Establishment; for her this was enough to show that women were at least equal to men.

A more satisfying event in 1944 was the handing over of the RAE carburettor, on which Beatrice had spent so much development time from the beginning of her employment at the Establishment, to H.M. Hobson Ltd for manufacture to be fitted to Bristol Hercules and Centaurus engines, engines installed in several fighter and bomber aircraft near the end of the war. Still called the "Hobson-RAE Master Control Injector", the unit was further adapted for use on many civil aircraft and gave excellent service, mainly on Bristol engines, for many years after the war.

His formal training completed, George moved with his crew to 625 Squadron, I Group Bomber Command, based near the hamlet of Kelstern in Licolnshire on September 13th, 1944. "A muddy, happy-go-lucky place", a former member of the Squadron recalls, remembering

George as reserved and quiet, but always listening to other pilot's talk about "ops". The airfield lay on higher ground than the village, and had more than its share of snow in winter and low cloud throughout the year. Grimsby, 13 miles to the north, the popular social venue, was not easy to reach but airmen grouped together to squeeze into a car or took a Starkeys bus to go to a dance or the pictures. George noticed that as aircrew got through half or more of their "tour", they became less sociable, and drinking in the mess became their chief recreation.

Training did not stop when aircrew started to fly missions over Germany or occupied territory; George flew "Dawn Patrols" alongside experienced crews of 625 Squadron, getting to recognise his Flight and its personalities in the air, before he was listed to report for pilot briefing for his first operation. There was no build up ; his crew appeared on the Battle Order for October 3rd, to fly with eleven other Lancasters from Kelstern, briefing times to be notified, provisional call for crews at 2.30 a.m.

This was a daylight raid, and joining up with 240 Lancasters from other squadrons and 9 target marking Mosquito fighter-bombers on the way to the target, 625 Squadron bombed sea defences on Walcheren Island, part of the German heavy gun defences of Antwerp. George's aircraft arrived at the target area on time; his bomb aimer was so pleased with the apparent accuracy of his bombing that he would not allow George to turn away from the bomb run until he was sure that the cameras which were now fitted to bombers had fully recorded their hit, by which time German anti-aircraft fire – "Flak" – was close enough to chip a propeller and make a small hole in one wing. George dived and turned out of the Flak to head back to Kelstern, furious with the bomb aimer for a moment. But then, he told Beatrice, "I was tremendously elated, for now I feel that I have done something to justify my mistakes."

On his second operation his Wing Commander flew with him as "Second Dicky" to make sure that George was really in control and confident. The raid on Saarbrucken met flak and enemy fighters, but losses were relatively low, at three Lancasters from the 531 that took off, and George returned with his newly boosted morale unshaken. Kelstern was covered in cloud, which was also low over the alternate landing airfield at Fortishall. "I was far more worried about icing up in cloud on the descent or bumping into another Lancaster." Returning to airfields after operations could be very dangerous, particularly when cloud was low. There was no official order of return, but pilots were briefed as to route, altitude and speed – observing for "ditched" aircrew if they passed over the North Sea. If visibility was poor or a pilot's concentration slipped, collisions could occur on the approach at a height at which parachutes were useless. George reported more than one near miss at the end of an operation, but he assured Beatrice of his care in avoiding potential dangers such as icy cloud and close flying, and reported "light flak and no fighters" after most raids.

His sixth operation, Stuttgart, on October 19th, had "no particular problems". His seventh, to Essen was very different: the Meteorological ("Met") report was of good conditions but there was low cloud all the way there and back. 1055 aircraft flew to Essen in these conditions, the Lancasters which formed the majority having no windscreen wipers to improve visibility in rain or cloud. The bomb aimer twice warned George of dangerously close Lancasters, the second time in a scream which omitted the position of the threat, so George guessed, dived and hoped for the best. As he turned into the bomb run, the rear-gunner saw a Focke-Wulf

Fw 190 on their tail and called "corkscrew Starboard", the urgent signal to the pilot to take immediate evasive action in a series of twists, dives and climbing turns in a forward, horizontal direction. The enemy fighter, travelling 100 mph faster than the Lancaster, could not follow these manoeuvres and would rush past, hopefully catching some of the gunfire aimed by the rear and upper gunners of the slower aircraft.

At the end of October, George had completed ten operations of the thirty that constituted a tour of duty. Ten operations in twenty-eight days, some nearly seven hours in duration, needing constant vigilance in the cloud that prevailed on most days that autumn, seemed to calm George and concentrate his mind on the business of flying his Lancaster and overseeing his six crewman. A gift for flying aircraft seemed less important than good assessment of risk, a talent for navigation in cloud and the ability to make a quick decision. His favourite part of each operation was reaching the target and the bomb aiming run, not because he took particular pleasure in killing, but because the excitement and concentration of dodging flak and fighters and achieving arrival at exactly the planned minute blotted out the greater fears that the long journeys to and from the target held for him.

He was most unhappy that Lancasters, which had already been lightened by removal of some of the armour plating intended to protect crew members, were required to carry bomb loads which took the aircraft 1600 lbs over the maximum weight stipulated in the pilot's manual. His feelings of insecurity were made worse by the need for massed bomber forces to fly slowly on the outward journey to allow every aircraft to position itself in the final bomb run at exactly the right time, in the right sequence. Several times an early start or misjudgment by the navigator forced

George to drop below 140 mph to avoid arriving ahead of time at the target, 20 mph below the recommended air speed for a loaded aircraft. "I hate the outward journey, that feeling of being balanced on a pinhead miles high is very pronounced with a fully laden bomber," he wrote in a letter to Beatrice.

The problem was made worse by George's dislike of slipstream, the wake that an aircraft, particularly one with four engines and weighing thirty tons, creates behind it. Slipstream produces turbulence in air up to a mile behind large aircraft; it caused following aircraft to jolt and momentarily drop, often to a position with one wing lower than the other that needed delicate but immediate correction. Finally, in bomber formations of 500 to 1000 aircraft, slipstream was absolutely unavoidable. George began to suffer from blocked ears, an old problem going back to his schooldays, while flying, and arranged an appointment with the Squadron Medical Officer on November 8th. The doctor gave him a "Thermogene jacket" to keep his chest and back warm and unspecified medicine three times daily. Four days later the doctor told George that he thought his treatment was not working, and he wanted to take him off flying until the condition was fully cured.

George was not prepared to accept this and in the discussion that followed, the MO learned something of George's dislike of flying a loaded bomber at low speed at high altitude, and drew George out to admit to a general discomfort at great height. *"He then asked if I wanted to come off flying for good. I said that meant going LMF (Lack of Moral Fibre) and I wasn't doing that."* The MO insisted; he believed that LMF associated with fear of high altitude was much less serious than fear of flak, and suggested that it was unfair to George's crew for him to go on. George disagreed; he knew the part of each flight that he hated, but he could cope and his crew would be no

less safe than before. *"It's an awful temptation, Trixie darling, but I can't do it. How would I have yours and my respect if I quit now? I have done 10 trips and there is a war on. I cannot expect to go through without trouble even if it is only nervous strain. What do you think about it?"*

Beatrice did not believe that George's ear problems were anything to do with his fear of flying in outbound formations, as 625 Squadron's MO seemed to think, and she urged him to see a specialist. But she did not think he should give up flying. "Darling I think you are right, if you can stand it you should complete your tour unless the ear specialist turns you down flat. I am very strongly tempted to say get out of it while you can but we wouldn't like it and both of us would be dissatisfied afterwards." George refused to accept the MO's suggestion and the visit to an ear specialist never materialised. He made himself available for the next bombing operation.

The term "L.M.F." – "Lack of Moral Fibre" – was part of the Armed Services' policy of treating admission of fear, or mental trauma caused by horrific experiences, as unnatural weaknesses, which carried a moral stigma. If it had any justification, it was that it was a way of preventing men from leaving at will the uncomfortable and dangerous occupation of fighting a war.

The reorganisation of Engine Department into the Power Plant Division reduced Beatrice's work load, in spite of her promotion and the extent of her authority over experimental work. She found time to work on some of the household maintenance and repairs that had been neglected while working under continuous pressure, and the work made her think how housework could be simplified by the application of engineering. She told George that utensils should be designed for easy use and repair, preferably by women who used them; floors should meet walls with a rounded skirting so that dirt and spiders could not collect. Here was a possibility for a postwar career – consultant domestic engineer. George entered into the spirit with his own ideas and sent Beatrice a sketch of his ideal home, a perfectly round house with a central rubbish shoot accessible from all rooms. He was more attracted to thoughts of some kind of motor engineering enterprise, which Beatrice also proposed rather vaguely, but he felt her ideas lacked substance.

"I don't quite know why you pick Bedford as the place we should go with excess engine factory plant and what we are to do on our own that will pay us sufficiently well. I certainly would like to be my own master (under you, of course) but everything in the design line seems to be very much a matter of team work these days. Still, I'll back you to the limit."

George was happy to let Beatrice think about how they could live without being civil servants. He claimed he was lazy and lacking in initiative; perhaps it was true, but he was very serious about being a Lancaster pilot. Four days after refusing to be taken off flying, he was heading for Dortmund for another raid, this time by 294 Lancasters in poor visibility. Six aircraft were lost. He was not pleased to learn when he returned that Beatrice had crashed the RAE Hillman on a slippery road on her way to Bristol, damaging the car but not herself – and that she was going to learn to fly. He told her she was a danger to herself on a bicycle, let alone a car, and that he definitely did not like her learning to fly

The Royal Aircraft Establishment had decided that some members of staff "should be familiar with and appreciate some of the problems a pilot faces", and asked Departmental Heads to nominate personnel for flying lessons. Those who accepted, including Beatrice, became the "Technical Flight" of the RAE, to start receiving instruction in February.

George hoped that by February 1945 he would complete his tour of 30 operational flights and come home on leave to Farnborough to make sure Beatrice was not taking unnecessary risks. He flew on three operations on three successive nights, the 5th, 6th and 7th of January, to complete 26 trips. After the third, an eight and a half hour flight to Munich and back, he was utterly exhausted, and depressed by the first casualty on his crew. His rear gunner, Flying Officer Freddie Rix, suffered severe frostbite in one foot when the heated air supply to the rear and mid turrets failed. His electric suit-heating also failed soon after take-off and F/O Rix said nothing rather than abort the flight. His foot was frozen through, there were further complications, and it was more than two years before he was able to leave hospital.

After Munich, winter closed in on Kelstern and there were no more operations for three weeks. Farnborough, too, had an exceptionally cold winter: Beatrice drained the entire water system at home every night through January and put five blankets on her bed at night. She told George that thinking that her bicycle chain had broken on the way to work, she looked down to see the back wheel spinning on ice while the machine remained stationary. The house was constantly cold. Beatrice had a warming pastime, which was pursuing spiders, which she hated, with a blowlamp. *"There are plenty of pockets of resistance in this house occupied by spiders so I decided a flame thrower was the only thing for under the sink."*

Beatrice tried to persuade George to take leave, but he wanted to be on base to make sure he did not miss a chance to fly and bring the end of his tour closer. His next operation, which was his 27th was not until February 1st. On February

7th when George had only two more operations to go, Bomber Command increased the tour of duty for bomber crews from 30 to 36 bombing sorties. Beatrice was outraged but George took it surprisingly calmly, unhappy though he was. He was not so happy that his 31st operation was the worst he had experienced. 625 Squadron sent 23 aircraft on February 13th to join a massive night raid by nearly 800 Lancasters on Dresden, the raid which later made some senior government leaders try to distance themselves from the area-bombing policy they had once created or supported.

The Dresden raid had a tactical purpose, as the city lay between Russian troops pushing from the east and Allied armies pushing from the west. 625 Squadron was briefed to bomb the main railway marshalling yards in the city to cut off supplies to German troops. It was also reported that German forces sandwiched between the western and eastern Allied advances were regrouping in Dresden. The troops had left when the raid started.

However, George was unaware of the enormous civilian casualties of the fire storm started by the bombs, and after leaving Dresden his navigator lost the planned route and took his crew over Nurnberg. Nurnberg was not bombed on that night, so George's Lancaster was the only British aircraft to appear above the flak batteries, and it received their undivided attention. "All hell was let loose. I spent seven minutes twisting and turning to avoid the flak, I expected every next second to be my last." Nothing hit him, to his astonishment. Then, back on track for the Channel, at 18,000 feet the aircraft started to drop and continued to drop when George increased engine speed and boost. Ice had formed on the wings and reduced their lift, which George was able to restore by going down to warmer air at 4000 feet, where the ice melted.

Five more "ops" left to do; in the worst of these, twelve Lancasters were shot down over Dortmund, one of which was carrying the crew who shared his hut at Kelstern, in sight of George's aircraft. Finally, on March 1st, he returned from his last trip, to Mannheim, and enjoyed the ceremony allowed to pilots after their last operation – "shooting up" the aerodrome. He proudly told Beatrice that his "shooting up" was admired at the celebration afterwards in the Sergeants' mess, and that his crew, who all had more operations to fly, begged him to sign on for a second tour as their skipper.

But there was no question of this. There were bomber aircrewmen who volunteered for a second, even a third tour of duty, even a very few who survived three tours, but George never considered it, and Beatrice heartily agreed with him. She knew better than him that the mathematical probability of surviving even one tour was not good, although German fighter defences had declined greatly since the most dangerous years of 1940 to 1943. Even so, 625 Squadron lost 18 aircraft while George was serving as a pilot. She wanted him back home with her after the war, and did not care whether it would be as a test pilot, an RAE "boffin" or just at home. These three possibilities as well as Beatrice's vague idea of an engineering partnership had all been discussed. Although George's postwar employment would seem the most serious concern, the two topics which took up more of their correspondence than any other as the end of the war approached were sporting transport, and babies.

Beatrice and George bought a 1932 12/60 Alvis saloon from Bill Boddy, the founder of Motor Sport magazine and unchallenged historian of Brooklands. He and Beatrice had met at Brooklands and later at the Royal Aircraft Establishment, and had a mutual friend in her young colleague, Bob Newton. Boddy wrote: *"I want £40 for it but don't quite know how to get it to you. I may be at Raymond Mays on Sunday but I would rather like to get home in it. I could rail it, or drive it half way down to you."* Somehow collection was arranged, and George used the Alvis at Kelstern and brought it back to Farnborough after the war, while Beatrice sometimes used her ex-racing Norton, more often cycling to work. She was very keen to resume motorcycle or car racing after the war and believed that the Lagonda Rapier, an advanced design using a twin overhead camshaft engine, but heavy for its 1104cc engine, would lend itself well to rebuilding into a competition car. She even suggested a "double Rapier" using half a Napier Rapier aero-engine (16 cylinders arranged in an "H" giving 400 bhp) which amused George, who wondered how the front wheels would be kept on the ground.

As for babies, Beatrice was not sure how she felt about them. She had definite ideas about the education and training of the young for early self-sufficiency, and enjoyed making sturdy toys for Biddy and watching her cope with them. She was more vague about the demands of early child-raising, but surely a baby could be no more trouble than a temperamental Velocette? George took an accountant's view:

"I consider that if you have children then (1) you will have to pack in your career for all time; (2) our finances would be in a precarious state for the next 20 years or so and such things as motorcycle and car racing would have to be cut out. I know you hold the view that children should be busy enough to earn their own education, but I don't agree . . . If you really want children then I consider that you should have a trial period of one year with you at home and see if we can cut our expenses to what they would have to be if we had children."

This was not an expression of fatherly instincts and a week later Beatrice, in her first enthusiasm of learning to fly, wrote: "I think all being well I'd rather have a Moth or a Magister than an infant. If I got a ground engineer's licence it shouldn't cost too much to run. Can I have one?"

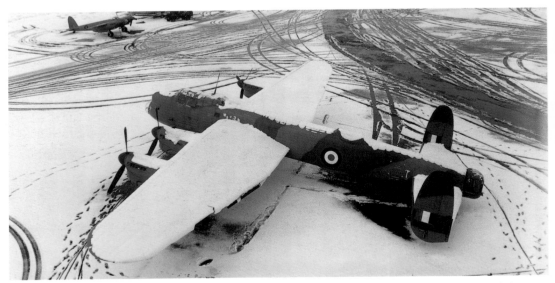

The bitterly cold winters of the last two years of the war are illustrated by this photograph of the airfield at the RAE. The Lancaster nearest the camera will need its cold starting aids to fire up the Merlin engines. *DERA, Farnborough*

A Lancaster II above the clouds. The defensive gun positions can be seen at front, at the mid-upper turret and at the rear turret. The pilot sat up in the main cockpit with the navigator and flight engineer, with the bomb-aimer below and in front of the pilot. *Royal Air Force Museum, Hendon*

George Naylor's crew were about half way through their tour when this picture was taken (Winter 1944), and the strain shows on their faces. On the front row, left to right: Flying Officer Jimmie Joiner – navigator, Flying Officer George Naylor – pilot, Flight Sergeant Reg French – wireless operator/gunner. Back row: Flight Sergeant Don Beadon – bomb aimer, Sergeant Stan Lavender – rear gunner, Flying Officer Freddie Rix – mid-upper gunner, Sergeant Lou Sunderland – flight engineer. *Gerald Rix*

A happier moment as George relaxes with his sister Edith at the family home in
Yorkshire. *Bryn Tennant*

Ten

The Jet Age

On May 7th 1945, General Jodl, Chief of Army Staff, communicated Germany's unconditional surrender to the Allied Supreme Commander, General Eisenhower. The news was quickly followed by wild celebrations throughout the United Kingdom and liberated Europe. Victory parties filled homes, streets and much of central London with delighted civilians and servicemen and women; schools were closed and licensing laws were suspended for a long day of dancing, drinking and bonfires. Beatrice had planned to join George at his Squadron at Boscombe Down on V-Day, celebrating by riding over on the Norton with open exhaust, but George was having medical attention to a persistent ear and nose infection and Beatrice stayed in Farnborough. But Muriel and Biddy were back in the house at Ashley Road, with Desmond, already back from his German POW camp, and Muriel made sure that V-Day was properly recognised.

On August 14th, 1945 Japan formally capitulated. The war was over at last. Air Chief Marshal Sir Arthur Harris, soon to be maligned for directing a policy laid down by the most senior staff of the Air Ministry and supported by Churchill, sent out a stirring message of appreciation, in the form of a Special Order of the Day, to the surviving men and women of Bomber Command. He praised their staunchness during long, dark, and dangerous hours in action, and the vital work of every support service, from photographic reconnaissance to runway construction.

George was transferred to Boscombe

Down in March 1945, to fly Avro Lincoln bombers, a larger version of the Lancaster with a greater bomb load, but before long he was grounded again by his ear problems. He hoped to transfer to Farnborough as a test pilot and repeatedly urged Beatrice to talk to the right people to achieve this ambition. But there was no shortage of test pilots, in spite of extremely hazardous and sometimes fatal attempts at Farnborough and elsewhere to break the sound barrier with Spitfire and Tempest aircraft. After months of maddening inactivity George was finally released from the RAF late in 1946, to return to Structures Department at the RAE, where he worked with success and distinction until he retired.

For staff at the Royal Aircraft Establishment at Farnborough the future was uncertain. The Establishment had doubled its staff for war work; now the impoverished state of Britain's economy meant possible closure, at least radical staff reduction. Sir Stafford Cripps had addressed senior staff at Farnborough in March 1945 about a brighter future in a new National Aeronautical Establishment at Bedford, but most of his audience would have preferred better pay at Farnborough and a wider appreciation of their work. The Establishment stayed where it was, but within twelve months the number employed had been reduced to around 3000, half its wartime strength.

Beatrice was still one of them, though there were many times when she wished she was not. The termination of advanced piston engine research was a serious blow, as her experience and reputation were built on her unique understanding of piston engine behaviour in extreme conditions. Instead of being in demand to solve urgent problems, she was someone for whom a place had to be found in the RAE, although outside, in the RAF and the Ministry of Supply she was still much respected. In a CV of her own career written in 1964 she she summarised her work in the immediate post-war years:

"From 1945 to 1949 I was attempting to do experimental work on combustion but as I never had more than one Assistant Technical Officer working under me I was unable to do much more than assist one of our chemists in his experimental work. As I was given numerous jobs connected with plant, organisation and training of junior staff etc. I made little progress on the combustion experimental work."

This brutal compression of four years' work shows her dissatisfaction with that period, but hardly gives a fair account of what she did during them. It had become clear quite early in the war that equipment available for testing engine "ancilliaries" – hydraulic and pneumatic equipment, fuel systems, pressurisation and cabin conditioning plant, was not up to simulating the greatly increased airspeeds and altitudes that were now being reached by the most advanced aircraft. A new High Altitude Test Plant was projected, and Beatrice had the responsibility of specifying and later commissioning and testing much of the new equipment for this unit. She worked with BJ Thorpe, MICE (Member of the Institution of Civil Engineers) who designed the building for the RAE, and it was not until after the end of the war that the Plant was complete and ready for commissioning.

Ironically, the piston engines for which it was intended were no longer of interest to the RAE. Nevertheless, the High Altitude Test Plant could be and was used for equipment for jet-propelled aircraft, and later was used by Beatrice for her work on cabin atmosphere control and cooling of high temperature equipment and auxiliary power. The commissioning of the heavy equipment, compressors, pressure vessels, cooling plant and the instruments to control them, some of the most sophisticated of which were "salvaged" from the Hermann Goering Institut in Germany, was highly classified work, much of it done by Beatrice between 1947 and 1950.

It was hoped that her experience with fuel flow systems for extreme conditions would help with controlling the combustion of fuels far more explosive than high octane aviation spirit, fuels such as the hydrogen peroxide/hydrazine hydrate propellant used by the German rocket interceptor, the Messerschmitt Me 163B. The two components of this fuel ignited immediately on contact, the force of this ignition ranging from the controlled continuous burn that shot the Me 163B toward its target, to the devastating explosion of an uncontrolled mix, which destroyed several Me 163Bs and their pilots. Beatrice was to work with this fuel in 1946 and 1947. She also looked at other potential fuels, one of which was aluminium powder.

Her assistant at this time was Tom Bowling, later to become Engineer in charge of Aircraft Engine Servicing and Maintenance at Rolls-Royce. He recalls:

"I was given the job of burning powdered aluminium in a combustion chamber and we decided that it would have to be sweat cooled, i.e. some liquid (water to begin with) seeping through a porous surface. I started with a single tube of the material fed with aluminium powder at one end and ignited with a calor gas/air flame with excess oxygen for the aluminium powder. Aluminium was chosen as it has a high calorific value/weight or density ratio. Boron would have been better but was not available.

"It worked but produced clouds of white smoke so that I had to get permission to light up from the Air Traffic Control!

Later I got a "proper" combustion chamber with convergent-divergent nozzles. Unfortunately, difficulties with cooling and with the solid products of combustion brought the experiment to an end."

During these trials aluminium powder tended to wander and the "RAE News" commented admiringly on Beatrice's "aluminium suit". Later, Beatrice recommended Tom Bowling for the RAE Technical Flight. Unlike her, he proved to have a natural aptitude for flying, and made quick progress from "circuits and bumps" to stall turns and spins. Beatrice observed this and although she had flown solo long before Tom, she asked for his help in sorting out her inability to master stall turns. This unembarrassed recognition of a junior's special talents did much for the morale of her team.

In 1947 she was transferred to the Supersonics Division of Aerodynamics Department, her second transfer in two years. "Aero" had been commissioned to carry out a major project and Beatrice was asked to supervise work on its motive power. The project was the tail end of a venture which should have made Britain the pioneer of manned supersonic flight.

Four years earlier, in 1943, the Miles Aircraft Company accepted a Ministry of Aircraft Production specification for an aircraft capable of reaching 1000 mph at 36,000 feet. The Company designed a small aerodynamically efficient machine, using strong, ultra-thin wings at right angles to its fuselage. The structure of the wings, the most critical part of the design, was finalised after tests on a conventional Miles aircraft, and Miles then built a full-size model capable of housing the latest development of the Rolls-Royce Avon jet engine. By this time the Directorate of Scientific Research had seen the near-supersonic Messerschmitt Me 163 interceptor with swept wings, as well as various advanced German projects for fully supersonic aircraft which all had swept back rather than straight wings. Advised by Barnes Wallis, now a research director of Vickers Aircraft, and influenced by several fatal crashes by pilots attempting to go through the sound barrier in piston-engined machines, the Directorate ordered Miles to stop work on the M52. As the project was government funded, Miles had no choice but cease development, and they were told to hand over all their designs, calculations and test data, which were sent on to the United States. The cancellation, unexplained at the time, was a shattering blow to Miles' design team, and eventually, to the company's future.

Using thin straight wings at right angles to a fuselage similar to that of the M52, an American Bell XS1 became the first aircraft to fly at supersonic speed, reaching Mach 1.015 (670 mph) in October 1947, less than a year after the M52 was cancelled. The wings showed no signs of instability or weakness. The similarity to the M52 was too close for coincidence.

The Ministry of Supply did not change its mind, but followed Barnes Wallis' proposal that supersonic tests should be carried out with radio controlled 3/10th scale models, and it gave a contract to Vickers (not to Miles) to construct and test six different supersonic designs, some straight wing, some swept wing. The Royal Aircraft Establishment was to assist in the exercise, and Beatrice was to supervise the development of a suitable rocket motor. A strong team, which included Bob Newton (the brave observer of the methanol/Merlin trials), Alan Barker and Norman Gilbert, started to develop the Alpha Rocket motor for remote firing. They designed and constructed most of its components in cooperation with the Mechanical Engineering section of Structural and Mechanical Engineering Department, soon to be separated as ME Department in its own right. The fuel was the combination of hydrogen peroxide and hydrazine hydrate with methanol already described and basically that used by the Messerschmitt ME163. The RAE report AERO 2215 reassuringly said "these fuels require careful handling, but it may be noted that with suitable precautions they are perfectly safe".

Beatrice was particularly concerned with the delivery of fuel in this rocket motor, as the two components needed to be fed in the right order, and with exactly the right timing to avoid producing an explosion instead of the thrust required. AERO 2215 reported that "During development a number of explosions occurred on starting". These could not always be explained as the evidence was usually in shattered bits of torn metal, but the wrong sequence of feed, and the accumulation of residues were the usual suspects. In case visitors to the development site should be in any doubt as to the explosiveness of the bi-component fuel, one of the development team would be happy to release a drop of fuel into a steel 40 gallon drum, followed by a drop of hydrogen peroxide to produce a satisfying bang, enough to make the drum wobble or leave the ground, according to the size of the drop.

Unfortunately this problem was never fully overcome. The flight test plan was to attach the model to a Mosquito fighter-bomber, just under its bomb doors, and after taking off from St. Eval in Cornwall, the Mosquito would fly out to sea and climb to 36000 feet, release the model, and fire it remotely when it was a safe distance from the aircraft. Beatrice went to Cornwall with some of her team to prepare the motor for flight. To cut a long story short, the trial flights were a series of disasters, from forceful separation of the model from the Mosquito when it entered severe turbulence followed by its complete disappearance, to explosion after release. Fortunately no one was hurt. Finally,

after test ground firings and modifications aimed at ensuring ignition when required, rather than at random, the Mosquito took off on October 10th 1948. At last the rocket motor ignited just as planned and the model shot away to be measured at Mach 1.38 in level flight, its wings remaining firmly attached. All of the £500,000 allocated by the Ministry to this test had been spent on the first design to be tried. No money was left to move on to the five other configurations originally planned as flying scale models and the exercise was abandoned as quietly as possible.

Infuriating though the supersonic project must have been, Beatrice relished a challenge which involved the release of high energy by machinery, whether in a bang or in steady generation of power. Although she did not work directly with Frank Whittle, nor for Power Jets at Pyestock, Beatrice was asked to help with fuel metering problems in early jet engines, and after the M52 episode she returned to "combustion" of solid and liquid rocket fuels. Her work centred on the metering and igniting of these fuels, rather than their chemical composition and led later to her involvement in another form of jet propulsion, the "athodyd" – short for "aero-thermodynamic duct", or ramjet.

First, however, Beatrice was awarded the Order of the British Empire in the New Year's Honours list in January 1948, for her work on piston engine research during the war. The number of letters of warm congratulation she received showed how many people of very diverse occupations felt the honour to be richly deserved. Well-wishers included Sir Stafford Cripps, Chancellor of the Exchequer, who had been Minister of Aircraft Production for the second half of the war; senior RAF officers; staff of the Ministry of Supply, and old friends and neighbours. The Women's Engineering Society sent its best wishes in an enthusiastic letter written by Dame

Caroline Haslett, the same Caroline Haslett who had helped launch Beatrice into an Engineering career twenty-two years before.

Beatrice was not the only woman working at the Royal Aircraft Establishment to receive an OBE – but there were few enough for this to be a proud day for her and the RAE. George, now back again at Farnborough and a Principal Scientific Officer, must have quietly glowed with pride, but he was not so happy when he was addressed as "Mr Shilling".

The work Beatrice did on combustion coupled with her experience of fuel systems, led naturally to her involvement with ramjets. Some background to guided weapons research at Farnborough may help to explain the growing importance of ramjets to the UK defence capability after the second world war. In 1947 the Guided Weapons Department was formed to bring together the work of several separate teams that had been working on guided missiles of all types, some of them since 1944 when teams to study "Guided Anti-Aircraft Projectiles" were set up. This work resulted from the Government's plans to complement manned aircraft with ground-to-air guided missiles for the interception of bombers. Research started in 1944 was intensified and coordinated by the Ministry of Supply in 1946, and from several possibilities for missile propulsion, liquid fuel rockets and ramjets were chosen as the most suitable for the purpose. This purpose was to bring down an approaching enemy as quickly as possible after its detection by radar.

The RAF required a minimum range of twenty five miles for their anti-aircraft guided weapons, while the Army and Navy worked to ranges of up to twenty miles, which came within the capacity of liquid fuel rockets. Ramjets had an advantage over rockets in range and also in their use of less volatile fuels, once launched. Ramjets, like the gas turbine or jet engine, provide motive power by compressing air, mixing it with fuel and burning the mixture to provide a propulsive jet from the expanded gases which result. Unlike gas turbine jet engines, ramjets have no moving parts to compress engine air. They depend on their forward speed and the resulting "ram effect" of the air pushed into their intake to achieve compression. As a result the ramjet needs an air speed of over 1000 mph to generate enough net thrust to propel an aircraft or missile. Some other form of propulsion, usually rockets, must be used to boost the vehicle to the speed at which the ramjet takes over. At this point the boosting rockets separate from the vehicle, which continues flight under ramjet propulsion. These requirements make development and testing difficult.

To provide the necessary airflow to sustain burn, a ramjet test rig was mounted next to two Rolls-Royce Merlin 30 engines in the old Engine Department test building at Farnborough, and the airflow from their superchargers was ducted to the ramjet intakes. This rig was in use in 1947 and 1948 but it allowed study of three inch diameter ramjets only. These were too small to propel an armed operational missile so a new test bed was built on the edge of the Establishment's airfield. The pressurised air supply for this rig came from three unsilenced Derwent jet engines set up under a large corrugated iron shelter to keep the weather out. This rig allowed testing of a six inch ramjet.

Setting up and monitoring these tests, standing close to three jet engines at full blast was intensely uncomfortable. Even with elaborate ear protection, the vibration and shock waves produced were enough to nauseate the operator well before the maximum stint of one hour was up. In those days safety at work was not a factor and staff did not consider the long term effects of noise and vibration.

Events in Berlin and Eastern Europe in 1948 gave great urgency to the work on ramjets, as Russia showed its intention to rule these territories as her own and to demonstrate her power to the NATO countries. What would Russia do next? The Ministry of Supply, with the help of WGA Perring, Director of the RAE, looked very thoroughly at the guided weapons projects under development and arrived at an order of priorities aimed at the quickest possible completion of an effective anti-aircraft weapon. The Ministry was anxious to involve the aviation industry in guided weapons developments as future contractors to the Government, and senior management of Bristol Aeroplane Company (BAC), English Electric and Ferranti agreed to send teams to study work at the RAE before moving on to train staff to undertake missile development contracts. Senior staff from the three companies spent three months of detailed study in Farnborough before returning to their Companies with suggestions for the next step.

Toward the end of 1949 these was growing interest in ramjets for medium to long range missile development, and Beatrice's work on potential rocket fuels came to an end. In the CV she wrote in 1966 her note for September 1949 is terse but not illuminating: "September 1949. Transferred on paper to Rocket Propulsion Division, Westcott (on paper) but continued to work in Farnborough." It seems probable that her old friend JEP Dunning, who led development and design of ramjets at Farnborough, had drawn her into this work to help with the complex problems of fuelling and ignition to obtain good combustion efficiency.

At Bristol, engineers returned from their stay in Farnborough to recommend that a missile using ramjets should be considered for development. This led to collaboration with the RAE to produce and fly a test vehicle, to be constructed by BAC and to be powered by two six inch diameter ramjets designed by the RAE. This was the JTVI. Beatrice, who had often visited the Bristol Aeroplane Company on piston engine business, was transferred to Guided Weapons Department as head of the Ramjet Section in January 1950, taking over from JEP "Pat" Dunning who had been promoted away from Farnborough. Her job was to run static and flight tests on the JTVI's engines. In addition she monitored manufacture at Bristol of the fuel control block which fed the ramjet motors once the booster rockets had pushed the vehicle to supersonic speeds.

As with the bi-fuel M52 rocket project, the ramjet engine ignition system was one of the hardest parts of the JTVI to get to work as intended. The missile, launched by a cluster of eight small solid fuel rockets, was intended to accelerate from 0 to about 1000 mph in very few seconds, after which the rockets burned out. Beatrice's ignitor and fuel system had to get the ramjet motor to fire and burn stably before the rockets cut out. It would then be travelling fast enough to give sufficient thrust to accelerate the test vehicle when the rockets fell away. A very tight sequence, which led to failure on many of the test firings under the explosive forces of acceleration and the air turbulence caused by separation of the redundant rocket motors.

There were other problems besides synchronising ignition, ranging from poor structural strength to difficulty of separation of the boost rockets at burnout. In May 1950 the BAC team redesigned the JTVI to the Mark II, and further Marks followed as test firings showed up further problems. Many fundamental lessons were learned and the results were applied to Bristol's ramjet powered Bloodhound missile. In all, 73 JTVI test vehicles were fired in the course of development between February 1950 and April 1952, and many changes were made by BAC in layout and detail to the original RAE design. In July 1951 JTVI Mk VII successfully fired up its twin ramjets after rocket launch and gave enough thrust to carry on accelerating at supersonic speed.

The achievement of the first British vehicle to fly under ramjet power was celebrated at the Bustard pub near the Larkhill test range on Salisbury Plain by Beatrice and her JTVI team, with staff from the Guided Weapon section of BAC. More successful firings followed, giving encouragement to both BAC and the RAE to carry on research and development of more powerful ramjets. Although the war in Korea was coming to an end, there was still a lively fear in the West of aggression by Russia, in particular of nuclear attack by bomber aircraft, leading to a third world war. It was the era of local civil defence organisations, working without any serious resources, while those who believed themselves indispensable to the nuclear future had underground bunkers constructed.

Beatrice could feel pleased with the work of her Ramjet Section although a positive result had taken a long time to come. BAC could be expected to develop the ramjet-powered guided missiles which they would supply to the Armed Services, greatly improving the long-range defence of Britain. Beatrice looked forward to continuing work on ramjets, but this did not happen,

A new director, Arnold Hall, was appointed to the RAE in 1951, following WGA Perring's sudden death. Perring was one of the few senior executives at Farnborough who recognised Beatrice's gifts through her dry, almost truculent manner; his death, attributed to overwork, deprived Beatrice of a good friend and ally. Hall was not impressed by what he found at Farnborough. He believed that there was duplication of

research, too many scientists pursuing their own special interests and poor communication between Departments. Quite rightly, he determined to rationalise uncoordinated areas of research and development.

Guided weapons work was an obvious candidate for review. Changing strategic demands and progress with guidance, airframe and propulsion developments had already led to reorganisation of missiles research in 1946 and 1947, and the formation of an RAE Project Group to draw together the problems and findings of work on ground-launched and sea-launched guided weapons in 1948. Inevitably, projects continued to multiply in number. In 1950 ramjet work was being done both at Farnborough, under Beatrice, and at the National Gas Turbine Establishment at Pyestock, a few miles from Farnborough, each with their own ideas of how a ramjet missile should be designed. Hall determined to concentrate ramjet work at the Pyestock site and called a meeting of staff of the Farnborough Ramjets Section to announce the move.

Of a staff of around ten, all but two agreed to the transfer, for this was more than a simple change of workplace; it involved joining a new staff structure under a new employer. Beatrice refused to move, as did her colleague, Alan Earl. She had many good reasons to resist. Although she would keep her nominal rank, her future position in a new organisation was an unknown; she was leading a section in work which was stimulating and important; her very independent attitude to timekeeping and minor bureaucracy would not be tolerated at Pyestock, whose Head she disliked; and her journey to work would be much greater and could no longer be shared with George, who was still working (not very happily) in Structures Department.

Beatrice stayed at Farnborough, and the RAE. Not only that, but she persuaded

Arnold Hall that she should continue to monitor test flights of the JTVI with Alan Earl, and that Roy Hawkins should also stay with her to continue to analyse flight test results sent by BAC. This apparent victory was not quite enough for Beatrice; she went on using the ramjet test facility at Farnborough, with its three Rolls-Royce Derwent jet engines, to test-run changes to the JTVI ramjet engines made by BAC at Patchway. It was an activity that could have been calculated to infuriate the new Director of the RAE.

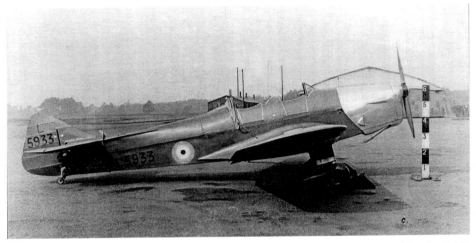

The Miles "Magister" monoplane trainer, used for training by the RAF and by the RAE for the Technical Flight. Beatrice learned to fly in it without experiencing any of the bad habits that George had warned her of. *DERA, Farnborough*

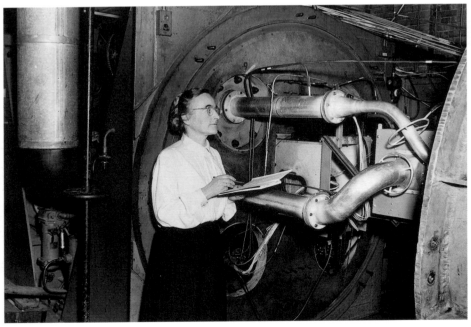

Beatrice poised to enter a crucial reading in the High Altitude Test Plant in a photograph for the *RAE News*. *DERA, Farnborough*

Heavy Duty vacuum pumps in the High Altitude Test Plant. *DERA, Farnborough*

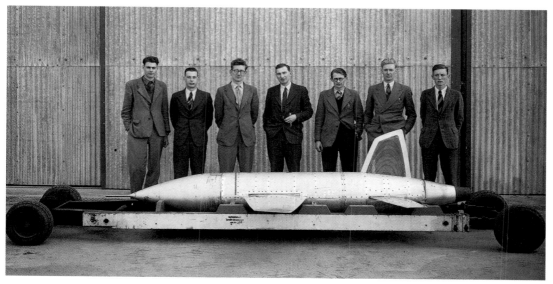

Farnborough 1947. The Vickers transonic test model based on the Miles design for a supersonic fighter – M52. Behind, centre AD Baxter, head of the project. To his left, R J Newton, jointly responsible for the development of the rocket motor. *R J Newton*

The Alpha rocket motor installed in the Vickers model. Three of the four ring-shaped tanks contain compressed air for driving the propellants to the combustion chamber. The large spherical tank holds hydrogen peroxide. Fuel (composed of methyl alcohol, hydrazine hydrate and water), is held in a tank which forms the nose of the aircraft. *DERA, Farnborough*

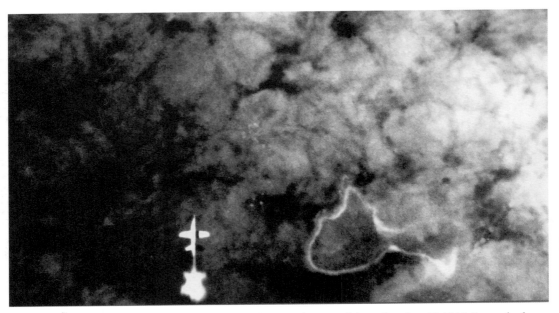

The moment of light-up of the rocket motor of the Vickers model on October 10 1948. It reached Mach 1.38 before disappearing into the sea. The Scilly Isles can be seen below. *DERA, Farnborough*

A much simplified diagram of a supersonic ramjet. Fuel is injected and burned in the duct, which if its forward speed is high enough, gives sufficient thrust to propel the missile. Other means, usually rocket power, are needed to take the ramjet up to at least the speed of sound before this happens. *Rolls-Royce Heritage Trust, Bristol*

The first RAE/Bristol Aeroplane Company ramjet, the JTVI Mk I on the launching ramp in 1950. Four of the eight launching rockets can be seen wired for ignition. At the back are the two six inch ramjet tubes. The test was for rocket separation only and exposed several problems. *Rolls-Royce Heritage Trust, Bristol*

July 1951. The MkVIII was a complete re-design of the JTV Mk I by the Bristol team. It fired successfully at launch and separation, the ramjets igniting and accelerating the JTV away as planned.
Rolls-Royce Heritage Trust, Bristol

July 1951. Beatrice and Alan Earl (on her right) join the ramjet team at the Bustard Inn to celebrate the first successful British launch of a ramjet, at the Larkhill range on Salisbury Plain. *Rolls-Royce Heritage Trust, Bristol*

Eleven

New Challenges

As soon as the last test flight of the JTVI series had been made, Arnold Hall closed down Beatrice's work at Farnborough on ramjets and later ordered the destruction of the ramjet test unit. Beatrice was transferred, on paper, to the National Gas Turbine Establishment at Pyestock, but having refused such a transfer in 1950, she declined to move a second time in 1952. She was not invited to join another Department for two months.

In January 1945 Beatrice had a serious row with GJ Armstrong, her new Departmental Head, over a minor difference of opinion, which she bitterly regretted. Writing to George, she said that she lacked the diplomacy and interest in pleasing superiors to "get on" in the Establishment. *"I tend to be too rude to my superiors or ineffective. I doubt if I'll ever get to the standard of some of the old hands at MAP or even half-way."* She would try harder. It seems that she could not change in spite of her good intentions, and in 1952 her prospects for promotion, which she dearly wanted, took a downward turn. She faced other obstacles; women were not regarded as Departmental Head material in 1952 at the RAE, any more than than they were elsewhere in government establishments. There was a certain "clubbishness" among some male senior staff, heightened by old school ties and golf club membership, which excluded women, and the Senior Mess at Farnborough was generally avoided by women although they had been "admitted" in 1944.

There were women at the Royal Aircraft Establishment who were highly respected, almost all for work in a specialised field rather than for their authority. Among them were Hilda Lyon, whose investigations started with the effects of turbulence and drag on airships in 1932, and later included study of the behaviour of swept wings as part of the preparations for supersonic flight. Another aerodynamicist was Frances Bradfield, who helped to complete the design of the Hawker Hunter jet fighter, while Ann Burns backed up her work on improving the stability of control surfaces – wing flaps, rudders and ailerons – with her own glider flying. She also flew in powered aircraft in search of the dangerous atmospheric condition known as "clear-air turbulence". Ann Burns also flew as technical scientific officer with a crew investigating the De Havilland Comet air disasters in one of the surviving aircraft.

During the war, there was Dorothy Robson, a specialist in bombsights, who, like Beatrice, spent time at RAF airfields introducing new equipment to aircrews and ground staff. She also flew in bombers to ensure that these sights were correctly fitted and calibrated, and was killed with the rest of the aircrew when a Halifax on a test flight crashed in Yorkshire hills in November, 1943. She was twenty-three years old. Her colleague in Instrument and Photographic Department, Brenda Rimmer, also flew regularly in the course of her work on airspeed and temperature measurement in a variety of aircraft.

Beatrice looked for promotion, because she enjoyed leading a team engaged in useful work, because she needed the money for her motor sport interests, and because she believed that she deserved it. She did not have a close friendship with any of the women at Farnborough, but she seems to have been liked by most of them, who found her ready to help if help was needed. She is remembered with admiration but some perplexment. A comment, if not criticism, made by more than one was that her informal dress, usually the same corduroy trousers and jacket, its top pocket full of pens, with hair invariably scraped into a bun, did not go with her rank or ambitions. "She was the utter antithesis of what would now be called power dressing."

In March 1952 Beatrice was transferred to Mechanical Engineering Department, which was a medium sized department involved with most working parts of aircraft other than the airframe and motive power. ME covered auxiliary equipment of all kinds, including heating and cooling of cockpits and crew cabins and also oxygen supply for crew breathing at high altitudes. Her responsibility was to be for the cooling of high speed aircraft and the provision of life support for aircrew at high altitude. As bomber operating altitudes had doubled from around 20,000 feet to 40,000 feet since 1945, cabin conditioning advanced from an unsophisticated arrangement of oxygen containers and heated suits to sophisticated cabin pressurisation and heating. In September 1953 Beatrice considered the possibilities of generating oxygen from the surrounding atmosphere during flight as an alternative to carrying the heavy storage tanks needed for full cabin conditioning. She came to the conclusion that the complex equipment that could do the job needed much development to reduce its weight and increase its reliability, and in her report recommended the use of liquid instead of gaseous oxygen on high altitude aircraft, as smaller, lighter storage containers cold be used.

In Spring 1954, Beatrice decided to seek promotion in the Scientific Civil Service outside the RAE. She applied for the post of Assistant Director, Research, in the Directorate of Engine Research and Development in the Ministry of Supply. Perhaps because of her lack of jet engine experience, or perhaps because of an unfavourable reference from the top of the RAE, she was turned down. She must have been very disappointed, but this did not stop her from studying to make herself the heat transfer expert of Mechanical Engineering Department.

The High Altitude Test Plant, thought by some to be chief among the RAE's white elephants, proved useful by providing some of the conditions for testing Beatrice's temperature control work. She helped to design and commission a cooling laboratory attached to the HATP to develop heat dispersal systems, work whose importance increased with every advance in aircraft speed. This was because at piston-engined aircraft speeds (up to 500 mph) the surrounding air can provide natural cooling for the engine and aircrew, whereas at a speed of Mach 2 (approximately 1500 mph at sea level) friction increases the surrounding air temperature to over 200°C. At Mach 3 this temperature is more than doubled, creating a vital need for cooling equipment. The laboratory was used for passenger cabin work on Concorde.

Beatrice investigated these problems and their solution with great thoroughness and produced a report, "Cooling Problems in High Speed Military Aircraft" for the working party on high speed aircraft cooling in 1956. She received Ministry permission to present this as a Paper to the Institute of Refrigeration, for which she received the Institute's Lightfoot Medal. Her work on cooling was recognised by the RAE with promotion to Senior Principal Scientific Officer, Individual Merit, an advance in salary and status but not in authority. She described the promotion as being "relieved of responsibility for all staff", in other words, a promotion to do important research without ruffling anyone's feathers.

She was not dedicated to ruffling feathers, it was more a matter of making sure that people were made aware of their errors in simple, unambiguous language. She was quite happy to work as part of a large multi-departmental team, such as the one assembled to find the cause of the Comet passenger aircraft crashes in January and June 1954. Both aircraft disintegrated at high altitude without warning, with the loss of all crew and passengers, a disaster for those on board and for the world's first commercial jet airline service. George, as a structures scientist and Beatrice, with her wide knowledge of high altitude functioning of auxiliary machinery in aircraft, were among those called in to help in this high priority investigation.

The wreckage of one aircraft sank in Mediterranean waters a mile deep, and was beyond recovery. The wreckage of the other, which crashed near Elba, was recovered from a depth of 600 feet and reassembled with infinite care at Farnborough before undergoing a minute physical examination. This finally established a window frame failure as the cause of the accidents. Beatrice had a theory that part of the cabin pressurising system that limited the pressure in the aircraft had iced up, allowing a build up of pressure that found the weak spot in the cabin window, but this was not proved.

George and Beatrice moved in 1955 from "Carfield", Ashley Road, Farnborough to a larger house on Prospect Road in the same town. "Ravenswood", number 64, was well suited for George and Beatrice's shared interest in fast cars and motor racing. Beatrice had competed in several South-Eastern Centre motorcycle trials in 1950 and 1951, but by 1955, after an accident which briefly hospitalised her, motorcycle sport was completely replaced by cars. One of the back rooms usually described by estate agents as a "reception room" was converted into an engineering workshop, equipped to professional standards, with all the tools needed to rebuild cars and their engines attached to metal plates on the wall. Visitors to "Ravenswood" were surprised to see a full-sized lathe on a concrete base dominating the room.

Beatrice kept one or two of her motorcycles, and when Muriel's daughter, Biddy, now sixteen, was persuaded to stay with Beatrice and George in Summer of 1958, she was given motorcycle lessons in return for keeping house and cooking for the couple. Years later, Biddy Fraser-Davies described the experience:

"B used to take me out to the hills where they did motorcycle scrambles before they went to work. She never allowed me to learn the blasted bike on a flat surface and had me doing hill starts on what appeared to be the middle of 45 degree slopes. She reckoned that by learning on rough ground, I'd really learn to ride the bike and then road work would be an absolute sinecure. Of course it didn't work like that because I was in such a state of absolute terror that I couldn't think!

"A lot of the time I spent at their house was a bit traumatic. B. and George were usually up all night taking apart their engines. It was always me who had to drive with George in his TR3. He drove too fast for me." She could not relax with either Beatrice or George, in spite of their good intentions.

Biddy in her teens and Beatrice's nephew David Woodford at about the same age were subjected to daunting cross-examination about their academic and other achievements, and Beatrice's conversational style, with long silences as she composed just the right trenchant comment, was not calculated to make a young person feel relaxed in her presence. But they recognised her desire to give really helpful information, and there were more than a few senior staff at Farnborough who were every bit as frightened of her when she was in a critical mood. Her niece, Janet, remembers Beatrice as a good aunt, riding and swimming with her and Nora's other children, Marion and David. She also recalls Beatrice, who had just been to Florida on RAE business, staggering up to their house in her usual unfashionable mackintosh, then emptying its many pockets of what seemed hundreds of Florida oranges that she had brought back for them. Beatrice assured Janet, the oldest child, that everyone had talent in some subject, which only needed to be found and developed. When Janet left school, Beatrice helped her to train to become a teacher.

Among her more obscure projects and one that must have given Beatrice great pleasure was an investigation into suitable engines for observation aircraft. These were not the ultra-high altitude sophisticated electronic spying aircraft that cause international embarrassment from time to time, but small, in some cases inflatable aircraft capable of being packed inside a 40 centimetre square box. They were designed to be dropped by parachute with secret agents, to enable them to fly, James Bond-like, to their objectives, and then home, or for military observers to rise above a field of combat and spot enemy locations. Code-named "Droopy", "Loopy", "Bunty" etc., these little delta-winged machines were to be powered by the lightweight engine most suitable for the task; Beatrice was to choose and evaluate these and to advise on their installation. Among the power units considered was one built by the ever ingenious motorcycle firm of Wooler, now near the end of its long involvement with engineering. The project was defeated by the low speed and instability of the inflatables, which did not provide enough cooling air for hard-working small engines. No doubt other factors also caused second thoughts, such as the

thought of agents trying to return safely from Russian-controlled countries in noisy little aircraft which struggled to reach 60 mph.

As the Cold War developed into a nuclear arms race in the 1950s, Russia and the United States moved on from experimental work on their stocks of captured German V2 rockets to ever larger, more powerful missiles, whose ranges were measured in thousands instead of hundreds of miles. The testing in 1952 by the United States of the first thermonuclear bomb created a potential of unimaginable destruction and accelerated the pace of development by the two "super-powers". Britain did not have the resources to keep up, but still wanted an independent nuclear missile capable, everyone hoped, of deterring Russia from making Britain the first target for attack.

The United States believed that Britain, recently a "Socialist" country with a Labour Government, was "weak" on Communism and not to be trusted with the most secret defence information, in particular on nuclear warheads. However there was an exchange of technology, mainly to the benefit of Britain, which included rocket engines, guidance systems and structures. Design of the Blue Streak British nuclear missile started in 1955, and by 1957 several Departments of the RAE were working on development and testing of its components. Beatrice was put in charge of heat transfer tests on a scale model of the missile's huge liquid oxygen fuel tank. The test equipment occupied a purpose built site on Jersey Brow on the RAE site,and was known as "The Boil Off Rig."

The aim of the tests were to investigate the behaviour of the liquid oxygen fuel and its container in heat, pressure, and other extreme physical conditions simulating a rocket launch and steady flight at high speed and altitude. A crucial question was how much fuel would be lost by evaporation during the launch, when heat generated by air friction would be at its highest – hence the "boil off" of the rig's title. Knowledge of this loss was essential to calculate Blue Streak's range and payload. A lengthy series of tests, reproducing each stage of flight and studying behaviour of every section of the tank was planned before the first test launching.

This was an important responsibility that took Beatrice out of the semi-academic role that her last promotion had handed her. She led a team of five which increased or decreased according to the demands of different tests. Few of them were aware that their work was connected with Britain's first nuclear missile, as staff other than senior scientists and division heads were not told the purpose of their individual tasks. The Royal Aircraft Establishment was a recognised "Secret Place" within the meaning of the Official Secrets Act.

One member of Beatrice's team who stayed with it until its work on the Boil-Off Rig ended in 1964 was Brian Kervell, who came in to assist with the collection, analysis and recording of test data. He went on to run the Mechanical Engineering Department Library, spending the last third of an almost full length Civil Service career as the curator and archivist of the RAE Museum. As someone who saw a sympathetic personality behind her severe appearance, Brian Kervell, very much her junior, was not overawed by her and over the years of Blue Streak work he was able to discuss general matters outside immediate work and discover her dry brand of humour. He recalls:

"One quirk of hers was her love of tea which she drank from the biggest mug I have ever seen We used to joke that lifebelts ought to be provided in case she fell in and drowned!"

Beatrice had no time for the Head of Mechanical Engineering Department, a man who was rarely seen, and she usually bypassed him to deal direct with the Deputy Director, Aircraft, Handel Davies. She needed a senior ally to fend off attempts to obstruct her freedom of action by Departmental Heads who disliked her independent way of working. She firmly believed that less staff at Farnborough would achieve more results. Talking about this with Brian Kervell, she did not go as far as the man whose answer to the question "How many people work at the Royal Aircraft Establishment?" was "about half of them," but she told him that his figure of 14% of all staff being superfluous was about half of her own estimate.

In 1962 she wrote and submitted an Internal Memorandum (No. ME252), "Memorandum on the pay of the Scientific Civil Service and the working conditions of scientists in this Establishment." In it she contrasted the pay and conditions of the administrative staff, the career Civil Servants who largely made up Divisional and Departmental Heads, with the Scientific Officers, who for the same length of service and with important development responsibilities, were paid less and had less leave entitlement. One can assume that she made her point in her usual forthright manner. Of 18 Reports, Notes and Memoranda that Beatrice listed as having written between 1936 and 1965, the Memorandum on the pay of the Scientific Civil Service is the only one untraceable in the RAE records archive or at the Public Record Office. It was not what the Director of the RAE wanted to hear.

Work on the Boil-Off rig continued in Mechanical Engineering as planned, along with other work done on Blue Streak by many other Departments and manufacturers, and over four years a great amount of data was collected, some of it leading to design changes, which in time would also need testing. Then, abruptly, in April 1960, it was cancelled as a military project. Brian Kervell remembers the day:

"We heard in the morning, Miss Shilling came out of her office (we were still in Q153 Building) and told us but we had to say nothing until the formal announcement in the House that afternoon. I think she had had one of her bouts of ill health but she had shrunk to even smaller size than I remembered (that was my impression) and her face was pale."

It seemed that Beatrice would never see a major post-war project successfully completed in Farnborough. The transonic/supersonic experiments, ramjets and now Blue Streak were all either cancelled or taken elsewhere. She had just been made Head of a small Division within Mechanical Engineering formed to cover Engineering Research; it now looked as if this had no further purpose.

In fact C Division survived the cancellation of Blue Streak, which was taken over by the European Launcher Development Organisation (ELDO) for peaceful scientific purposes. Blue Streak was successfully launched in June 1964 from Woomera, Australia. Beatrice continued cryogenic research and heat transfer work in connection with aircraft cooling, cabin conditioning and further studies of hydrogen-fuelled aircraft. In May 1964, Beatrice was 55 and would retire in five years time; now she was busier than at any time since 1943. Beside her work in charge of C Division, Mechanical Engineering, Beatrice represented the RAE on the Aeronautical Research Council's Engineering Physics Sub-Committee, and at regular intervals was asked to help Structures Department with accident investigations.

A Victor "B" Mk2 bomber crashed near Chicago late in 1959 for no observable reason. Beatrice concluded that the hydraulic drives to the main alternators were starved of oil by negative g in a planned violent manoeuvre, leading to total loss of power to the aircraft controls. She was very concerned that modern aircraft design should produce pipework for fuel, oils and coolant that would not be affected by freezing or the forces of inertia, writing "An Introductory Review of Engine Icing" to remind engineers of its dangers. Another cold weather peril was ice or snow on airfield runways. These dangers were very publicly highlighted in February 1958 when the British European Airways Ambassador carrying the Manchester United football team crashed on take-off at Munich, killing seven team members and eleven journalists and club staff. Beatrice was able to show that the cause was not failure by the pilot to clear his wings of snow, as thought, but by "drag" from slush preventing take-off speed being reached.

Near to the south west corner of Farnborough Airfield, Beatrice experimented with ways of making runways safer, specially for aircraft in a situation when take-off has to be abandoned and the aircraft stopped in a short length of runway. Brake Test Building north of this site housed a brake test apparatus, which allowed different sizes of aircraft landing wheels and their tyres to be run at speed on a drum which represented the landing surface. Wheel speed and resistance of the drum could be adjusted to measure the stopping power of different wheel/tyre combinations.

Beatrice pointed out that as aircraft got faster, wheels, and hence the tyre area in contact with the runway were getting smaller, putting greatly increased strain on the braking system. She calculated that the braking forces necessary to bring a Lightning jet fighter to a halt were almost eighty times greater than those needed to stop a Formula 1 racing car from the same speed. Yet a Lightning weighed only twenty-four times as much as the 1963 Grand Prix car. As aircraft speeds and weights were certain to go on increasing, Beatrice declared that improving tyre/runway friction, and improving braking systems were matters of immediate urgency.

To investigate runway friction, a surface was laid near the high speed rocket track at the edge of the airfield using materials which created greater friction with aircraft tyres than standard runway surfaces. Coarse grades of Macadam were found more effective than plain or grooved concrete, and redundant aircraft were provided, with wings cut short to prevent unintended take-off run tests. One particularly enthusiastic pilot managed to leave the ground in his cropped-wing Canberra without hitting the arrestor track, raising the comment from Beatrice, "Oh, didn't stop."

This work on tyre design and runway friction was followed with interest by other research establishments including NASA. Following a visit to the runway friction track by a USAF Starlifter transport aircraft in 1968, Beatrice was invited to the United States to take part in a NASA conference on all aspects of tyre and runway work.

In her final years at the Royal Aircraft Establishment she was engaged in cryogenic tests of insulating materials for liquid hydrogen rocket fuel tanks, in developments in cabin conditioning systems in the High Altitude Test Plant, in helping to design and build a bobsleigh for the RAF Olympic team, and in the runway safety work. She was consulted by outside organisations on a wide range of problems, from diesel motorcycle engines to grand prix car cooling, and served on several national technical committees. It was a happier, busier time than most of the 1950's had been for her.

In the middle of all this activity, Beatrice reached the age of 60 and obligatory retirement. In a career of thirty-three years she had adapted to many changes, not all of them welcome. In times of crisis she had avoided open mutiny, choosing to ignore instructions she did not want to hear; she had the intelligence and curiosity to emerge from each change of direction an expert, sometimes "the" expert, in her new field.

More than 200 people came to Beatrice's retirement presentation. Her choice of retirement gift was a trio of Canaletto paintings, in contrast to the taps and dies given to her on her marriage to George Naylor. Haydn Templeton, the head of Engineering Physics Department, as Mechanical Engineering was now called, presided over a cheerful occasion, in which Beatrice's achievements were recalled, including her skill in brazing pipework. She refuted, again, the story that she had personally turned her wedding ring from stainless steel on a lathe, and threw it on the table with a clatter for anyone to examine. As a parting shot, she praised the British aircraft industry for producing the best aircraft in the world, but blamed cancelled orders and late deliveries on an excess of management staff.

As well as the Canalettos, she was given a magnificent retirement scroll. Artistically illustrated, it bore the signatures of over 200 colleagues and well-wishers, and closed with two quotations:

"Happy the man who, void of cares and strife, in silken or in leather purse retains a Splendid Shilling." (John Philips, 1676-1709) and:

"The Shilling will shortly disappear from our currency – and its value will no doubt increase compared with the five new pence piece replacing it." (Anon, 1969)

The Royal Aircraft Establishment from the air, mid 1960s. *RAE, Farnborough*

Places of importance to Miss Shilling:

A   Engine Dept offices from 1942
B   Engine Dept fitting shop
C   Engine Test Beds
D   Engine Dept 'C' Flight offices. Base for staff
    engaged in engine related flight testing
E   RAE airfield control tower
F   Engineering Department where Beatrice had her
    office from 1952 to her retirement
G   Jersey Brow, location of "Blue Streak" fuel tank test
    rig
H   High Altitude Test Plant

The Blue Streak missile, seen here being prepared for launch at the Woomera range in Australia, was intended to be Britain's independent Ballistic missile. After several large research and development projects were well under way, Blue Streak was cancelled as a defence project. *DERA, Farnborough*

The "boil-off rig". Beatrice led a team that tested behaviour of a liquid oxygen tank in conditions of launch and flight. This is the test tank with power cables to tank heating on the left, and wiring to the monitoring instruments on the right. *DERA, Farnborough*

Aircraft retarding surfaces were tested at Farnborough by an English Electric Lightning fighter, with partly-blocked jet intakes to limit its speed. It still arrived at the test area very quickly. *DERA, Farnborough*

Still well on the move, the nose wheel has started to dig in, and the Lightning will now slow rapidly. *DERA, Farnborough*

Twelve

An Independent Woman

Beatrice looked forward to an active retirement. She had no interest in travel or golf and only a minor interest in her large garden. Her interest and pleasure in the theory and practice of engineering were as strong on the day that she retired as when she had been a student in Manchester, and frustration and disappointment at the RAE had not diminished them. Her idea of relaxation was to drive a fast car at full throttle, and if the car was not fast enough, her workbench was there in the back room to machine new parts to make them faster. George, three years younger, still had some years of work at the RAE before retiring, and he shared her interests as fully as ever. In 1967 the time came for both of them to renew their RAC Competition licences. Strangely, Beatrice's date of birth, sent in herself for her new licence, appears as 1918; at a stroke she had become six years younger than George and could look forward to another eleven years of motor racing !

In 1951 she took part in her last motorcycle competition, an off-road trial in which she rode a Tandon machine, the product of a small and short-lived company, powered by a Villiers two-stroke engine. It had, of course, been modified by her, but she fell off it awkwardly, seriously damaging her knee. Beatrice decided that this was the end of motorcycle sport for her, and from the mid-1950's she and George raced cars regularly as members of the British Automobile Racing Club. They still kept a changing collection of AJS, Velocette and Norton machines for their use. George and Beatrice were amateur club racing drivers, sharing a hobby with many hundreds of others, but their determination, their commitment and their adventures matched those of Grand Prix drivers.

Their first racing car was a creation – or re-creation of a classic sports car which provoked very mixed reactions on its first appearance. This car, a Lagonda Rapier, was a true combined effort. Beatrice had been impressed by the very modern twin overhead camshaft engine when she came across it at Brooklands before the war, and she and George looked out for one, unsuccessfully, during the war. They settled for a 1932 Alvis which George used as his "hack" at camp in the RAF, and by the end of the war this car had been more or less driven to death. In 1946 two Lagonda Rapiers were advertised at prices that Beatrice considered affordable, one a 1934 "fixed head" coupe, with 70,000 miles on the "clock", the other little more than a chassis and engine. *"We stripped everything and rebuilt it to our limits. The body was scrapped, we built a 2/4 open aluminum body. Redesigned it and modified it slowly between races."* This was Beatrice's summary of about four years' work, which converted a solid, heavy but elegant little saloon into a sparse aluminum-bodied racer, capable of around 100 mph. Many Lagonda enthusiasts were shocked at the conversion of a classic car into a special, but it would have been as much work to restore the Rapier to its original condition, and George and Beatrice were only interested in racing.

Recalling the car to Chris Wiblin of the Lagonda Rapier Register in 1987, George added more detail to Beatrice's summary of the conversion. The chassis, suspension components, body and interior were all completely stripped, and rebuilt to George's specification with new springs, bushes and body shell. The engine was rebuilt from scratch to Beatrice's plan, with new bearings, improved gas flow, larger SU carburettors and a new four pipe exhaust. The car was raced mainly on the Goodwood circuit, with many second and third places and the occasional win between 1955 and 1958.

Early in 1959 a new Austin Healey Sprite was bought and this was raced for three years, gradually being modified for more speed. Beatrice improved her time round Goodwood from 2 minutes 12.6 seconds to 1 minute 59 seconds. *"This was, apparently, my last race in the Sprite at Goodwood but I put in two practice laps on 8th April 1961 before George "blew up" the engine"*, Beatrice wrote in a summary of her car racing career in 1965 for the newly formed British Women Racing Driver's Club.

The last entry read:

"23rd June 1962. Members BARC race, Goodwood. Elva Mk VI Sports Racing Car. 1 m 48 secs in practice. Standing lap in 1m 50. CRASHED. Car written off, driver nearly."

This was a serious accident, in which Beatrice turned the car over at speed, fracturing bones in her shoulders and arms and crushing though not breaking her legs. The car had no roll bar. George added his own peppery PS.

"Statements indicate that she was virtually pushed off course by a clot who could not drive and who was determined not to be beaten by a woman. End of her racing driving, or is it ?"

Beatrice herself was more charitable about the other driver: *"He was an ex-RAF pilot, so he was too busy checking the instruments to look where he was going."*

Unfortunately it was the end of motor-racing for Beatrice, for after the accident

Beatrice found that the circulation of blood to her legs had been affected, leading to stiffness and pain which only showed itself to her colleagues by an increase in her rate of smoking. But this was not the end of fast cars in the Naylor household. George later listed the cars that had passed through their hands after the war, a cross-section, if not a catalogue, of British sporting cars:

"Wolseley Hornet, Morgan 4/4 open, Alvis 12/60 saloon, Riley 9 open, two Rapiers, Bradford, 1.5 Riley saloon, MGA 1600 open, Triumph TR3, Austin Healey Sprite which we really raced and modified as we had done the Rapier, 3.8 Jaguar E type, Elva FJ (Formula Junior racing car) rebuild as a Mk6 sports-racing car after I was involved in a multiple pile-up in the International FJ Final at Goodwood in 1961, Mini Minor, Mini Cooper, Triumph Vitesse, Triumph Dolomite, 4.2 Jaguar E type, Triumph Spitfire open, Ginetta with Imp engine designed by Coventry Climax; this Ginetta was promptly stripped completely by my wife, painted, modified and rebuilt as if we were to start racing again; perhaps we might have done but the work took about 5 years and by now I was developing cataract troubles."

George's mother was staying at the house just after his crash in 1961, and George concealed the evidence, a very bent Elva chassis, in the garden under a tarpaulin. She was very worried by their racing and found the constant "tinkering" with cars irritating. She stayed with her children in turn and complained to George that there was never a car around fit to take all three of them anywhere. It was in response to this that the Bradford, a noble but very pedestrian van built in Yorkshire, was bought. George had his final racing crash in April 1966, when his Mini-Cooper left the circuit on being shunted by another competitor. George was unable to work for two months and tried to take legal action against the driver, whom he accused of knocking him off the circuit.

However the British Automobile Racing Club firmly reminded him that such litigation was excluded by the terms of his Club membership. Beatrice continued working on the Ginetta, but neither of them were really fit to race by the time it was finished. Perhaps it was just as well in George's case, as the Ginetta was a very small car and he was a very large man.

In July 1967 Farnborough had two visitors Beatrice must have been very proud to meet. They were Dan Gurney, American racing driver and race-car manufacturer, and Harry Weslake, the designer of the Vee 12 cylinder engine that powered Gurney's Grand Prix car, the AAR Eagle. They brought with them the car with which Dan had recently won the Belgian Grand Prix at an average speed of just over 145 mph, but which had shown signs of over-heating. The car was due to race in the British Grand Prix in a few days' time. Dan Gurney recalls the visit.

"If I remember correctly, we were up against an engine-cooling problem and didn't have many options. The radiator was as big as I could get in the space allowed and we ended up putting "shark louvers" on top of the nose and "elephant ears" on the sides to help extract the hot air after it passed through the radiator."

They hoped to find an aerodynamic solution at Farnborough and Beatrice was one of those asked to advise. She studied the engine and its installation and suggested some alterations. What they were is lost to history, but the Gurney Eagle problems were not solved and Dan retired with mechanical troubles in five of the remaining six Grands Prix of the 1967 season. His car had been the fastest of the season's contenders, exceeding 200 mph in practice for the Belgian Grand Prix, but although he had many more successes in Indianapolis and sports car racing, the All American Racers Eagle Grand Prix car did not race after 1969.

Beatrice shared with George an irrational prejudice against "Yanks", a prejudice surprisingly common in wartime and post-war Britain. This was due partly to the very un-British self-confidence of Americans overseas, which was interpreted as a kind of boasting, and partly to reluctance to recognise America's vital part in winning the war. Some American servicemen did nothing to improve their image, but neither did all British ranks. Americans that Beatrice met personally in the course of RAE business were invariably approved of, as undoubtedly was Dan Gurney.

Returning to dirty fingernails and the lure of speed, in 1969 Beatrice bought an "E Type" Jaguar, the fastest sports car then for sale in Britain. This was the Naylors' second Jaguar, for George had rolled the first, ending up in hospital. The story was that Beatrice was so furious that she refused to visit George until someone convinced her that the accident was not his fault.

By the mid 1970s Beatrice and George were showing signs of age and of wear and tear from their motor-racing accidents. Both were heavy smokers and Beatrice's susceptibility to throat infections and coughs was probably not helped by years of working with a wide range of combustible chemicals. She was mentally tough and had been physically strong for her small size, with strong shoulders, arms and wrists that had held a racing motorcycle on line at speed over bumpy ground, and could tighten nuts on a machine that George had difficulty untightening. Shooting took over as their active pastime; this was mainly small-bore target shooting, but also included some rough shooting with ex-RAE friends, the "Old Uns", in woods around Farnborough. Both were good shots, and achieved very close groupings on targets. The rifles that Beatrice had kept in the house in case they were needed to fight off invading Germans disappeared, perhaps in one of the general appeals made by the Government just after the war to return weapons that had found their way into private homes.

In summer and autumn 1980, an exchange of correspondence in the Brooklands Society Gazette revealed some confusion between Beatrice Shilling, the one time motorcycle racer, and Beatrice Shilling, or "Schilling," the RAE "boffin." One of the letters is particularly interesting and is worth reproducing:

"C.E.Turner's enquiry (Summer Gazette) interested me as I met a Miss Schilling at RAF Farnborough in the late '60s. Apart from the difference of the small "c" it could have been the same family, if not the same lady.

"I had previously been told that she was the greatest carburettor expert in the country and normally I would have welcomed such an opportunity to discuss my Vauxhall Villiers which had three Zenith carburettors mounted on the blower.

"In the event I was present at Farnborough rather in the role of someone about to be carpeted. The interview came about through my connection with bobsleighing as captain of the British team. In 1964 Tony Nash and Robin Dixon had won a Gold Medal in the two-man bob in the Winter Olympics at Innsbruck, increasing British interest.

"The RAF had always been enthusiastic and successful bobsleighers and unknown to me had constructed a bob of their own design at Farnborough incorporating new ideas on suspension and steering. This was taken out to St. Moritz for testing by the RAF and other drivers. Unfortunately the Farnborough equipe's arrival clashed with an international race date, and although one or two runs had been made they were unable to use the track during race week.

"On my arrival at St. Moritz I was confronted by an enthusiastic but harassed group of technicians getting urgent calls from Farnborough calling for action and reports. I did my best to soothe things and explain the situation to Farnborough without much success.

"After the race meeting it became evident that the new bob was too lightly built to stand the hammering. Although it almost steered itself on the straights it was slow on the corners and the front and rear runners would not stay in line. I rode as brakeman on its last run to see what went on. At the finishing line there was no steering lock left and with that familiar scraping noise and a flurry of snow and ice the bob turned over.

"On return home I was summoned to see Miss Schilling at Farnborough to do a bit of explaining. There was not a lot one could say but it was worth the trip to hear Miss Schilling's personal assessment of various bob drivers she had met.

"If my spelling of the lady's name is correct it will at least avert any ghastly puns about how many shillings make a bob.

A.Brooke, Hampsthwaite, York."

The single identity of the two Miss Shillings was cleared up by letters from W Boddy and Bernard Harding, among others. The trial bobsleigh had not been designed by the RAF, but for the RAF by Beatrice and Alf Rivers, an extremely good draughtsman who had worked for Engine Department during the war. The request from the RAF Bobsleigh Association was welcomed by Mechanical Engineering Department at Farnborough, on the understanding that it would be constructed by apprentices of the Establishment and from AEC Ltd, which firm also produced most of the machined items for the bob, and that work on it would be done outside normal working hours. Beatrice took charge of the project, assisted by Alf Rivers, ES Hiller (another draughtsman), and Peter Harben.

The team produced an article on their plan for Design Engineering November 1968, in which Beatrice's firm tone can be detected. "Almost all European bobsleighs are built by Podar, an Italian blacksmith", it stated, and went on to describe the steering, suspension and aerodynamics of the most widely used bobs.

Beatrice proposed to use car-type (Ackerman) steering in place of a pivoting beam axle, and to use independent suspension of all four runners, again based on automobile practice. Streamlining of Olympic bobsleighs was very basic, and limited by the rules of the sport, but Peter Harben of Engineering Physics Department produced a smooth and simple shape for its monocoque (one-piece) chassis, and organised its fabrication by Specialised Mouldings, the constructors of Lotus Grand Prix car bodies. The component parts made by AEC and Engineering Physics Department were assembled by the apprentices at Farnborough from Alf Rivers' drawings, supervised and assisted by Beatrice and Peter Harben.

The budget for this project was extremely small, and Beatrice's ability to find tools and materials in unexpected places was very valuable, as was her ability to extract help from unwilling workshops. Once completed, the prototype had to be transported to Switzerland, a major budgetary problem, which Peter Harben solved by persuading his dentist (and friend) that towing a trailer carrying a bobsleigh behind his Rover 2000 would be the perfect way to drive to a winter holiday in Switzerland. The journey in midwinter with a trailer was not easy, as can be imagined, but it was completed safely. A Brooke's letter describes the disappointing sequel. Given time and financial backing, Beatrice's team would probably have modified their design according to the bobsleigh team's suggestions and made a highly competitive machine. Beatrice went on looking for sponsorship until 1971, two years after retiring from the RAE, but

never found enough backing to restart the project.

1969 was the fiftieth anniversary of the formation of the Women's Engineering Society. Beatrice had had close associations with the Society in the 1920s as a trainee electrical engineer, then later, reporting on life as a research student at Manchester to the WES journal, *The Woman Engineer.* While still working on rural electrification for Margaret Partridge's company, Beatrice agreed to break the Washington Convention restricting the employment of women at night to further the Women's Engineering Society's argument that women managers and technicians should be allowed to supervise night-time processes. The International Labour Organisation supported their case, and Beatrice was pictured, smiling shyly, with most of Margaret Partridge's staff, over the caption " Perpetrators of the Original Offence" in *The Woman Engineer.* Later on she served on the committee of the Society, and did her best to persuade young women that engineering was a career that could provide both progress and fun.

In December 1969, the University of Surrey conferred the Degree of Doctor of the University on Beatrice, along with five other candidates who had earned the honour for academic, artistic or corporate achievement. She was presented for the degree by Miss BE Stern, with a short speech that summarised her success as an engineer, in spite of "having the wrong sex for the profession of her choice". Miss Stern told her audience that Beatrice was still a member of the Physics Sub-Committee of the Aeronautical Research Council, and added that it was particularly appropriate that she had received her Doctorate in the Golden Jubilee year of the Women's Engineering Society.

Later, reading, and watching television, occupied more and more of Beatrice and

Unrecognizable as a Rapier but much quicker, the Naylor conversion at speed at Silverstone in June, 1957. Driven by Beatrice, it won the five lap Lagonda race. *LAT Photographic Archive*

While Beatrice fitted comfortably into the Rapier, George towered over it and gave it a weight handicap. He still won races on it. *Tony Wood*

The final version of the Rapier was even starker and its appearance did not please everyone. *Tony wood*

Dan Gurney (dark suit, third from the left) brought his extremely fast Grand Prix car to the RAE in July 1967 looking for help in solving cooling problems. Beatrice listens to Harry Weslake, designer of the car's twelve cylinder engine. *DERA, Farnborough*

Beatrice looks closely at the Gurney Weslake engine. Mechanical troubles prevented Dan Gurney from finishing among the leaders of the 1967 Grand Prix World Championship. *DERA, Farnborough*

The Royal Aircraft Establishment bobsleigh nearing completion at Farnborough in 1968. At the front is Alf Rivers the draughtsman/co-designer, who had once worked with Beatrice on the first batch of restrictors to be fitted to Merlin engines in 1941. *DERA, Farnborough*

From one engineer to another. Sir George Edwards, Pro-Chancellor of the University of Surrey and managing director of the British Aircraft Corporation, confers an Honorary Doctorate on Beatrice at Guildford on December 3rd, 1969. Standing next to her is Miss BE Stern, who formally presented her. *DERA, Farnborough*

Appendix 1

The negative gravity effect.

*N*otes on the behaviour of free surface fluids in aircraft, subject to changes in g forces with particular reference to engine carburettors.

By RJ Newton, former colleague of Beatrice Shilling at the Royal Aircraft Establishment, Farnborough.

Most fluid containers in aircraft (for fuel, oils, hydraulics, water, etc.) are not completely full of the relevant fluids; some are vented, some not, some have anti-slosh baffles but the volume above the fluid, sometimes at the start of a flight, but also during it, as the fuel is consumed, is replaced by air or gas; these may be at a higher pressure than that outside the container but this will not alter the behaviour of fluid due to changes in acceleration forces upon it.

In all such containers under these conditions, the contents will move, due to inertia, generally in the opposite direction to the acceleration forces in the container, the movement usually being complex since the force and its direction will rarely be uniform during a manoeuvre. So, not only will the bulk of the fuel move around randomly (slosh) but its surface will tend to break up into units and particles of smaller volumes, the magnitude of which at any moment will depend on factors such as the original surface area, the viscosity of fluid, and the number, shape and surface finish of any baffles present, especially above the fuel surface level. Some liberation of the dissolved gases may also occur.

The effect on fuel in carburettor float chambers.

In the case of float chambers, which are subject to the same changes in force and direction, and with particular reference to the SU AVT/40 series fitted to Rolls-Royce Merlin engines, the surface is even less stable, however smoothly the manoeuvre is executed. It is always turbulent due to its velocity and random direction through the needle-controlled entry point, to the flow around the floats, their control mechanisms and the irregular shape of the float chamber walls. A degree of stability is achieved only in straight and level flight at very small throttle openings when the float needle valves are very nearly closed, thus reducing the velocity through them to a minimum and, therefore, the likelihood of disturbing the fuel surface in the chambers by "jetting".

When the normal 1g downwards vertical force on the chambers falls to zero or beyond (i.e. to negative), and/or a horizontal component is applied, the fuel can surge, invariably non-uniformly, to the sides and roofs of the chambers, some of it exiting through the air vents to the venturis. If the exit holes are in the chamber floors, as in the standard ATV series of carburettors, these become momentarily uncovered, the engine is starved of fuel and can hesitate or sometimes cut – the so-called "weak (mixture) cut."

When this occurs, the floats, which simultaneously are subject to reverse buoyancy from the fuel which is now above them, drop to their lowest position thus losing control of the inlet needle valves, which are forced wide open by the resulting surge of fuel at full inlet pressure. This refills the space beneath the fuel, now at the top of the chambers, and quickly dispels the air (and some fuel) through the air vents.

The pressure in the chambers then rises to almost the same value (about 10 psi) and fuel deluges through the exit holes via the main jets and diffuser tubes, initially restoring power to the engine – but only very briefly. This is because the needle valves remain open under the force of the incoming fuel which is much greater than the opposing closing force provided by the floats, even though, by then, they are completely submerged. Flow to the engine, therefore, continues but at a prodigious rate which increases the mixture strength (air/fuel ratio) to levels far higher than the engine can burn – a condition widely known as "rich cut".

Neither condition, however (weak or rich, hesitation or cut), lasted very long; pilot combat experience varies considerably; some say that during violent manoeuvres, which included negative g, normal power was restored after about one and a half seconds whilst others believe that it took several seconds. Test pilots who sometimes had the benefit of g meters fitted in their cockpits, tend toward the lower figure but even then, under closely controlled conditions, it must have been very difficult, in such short periods, precisely to identify what was happening to both the aircraft and the engine.

As far as I am aware, no recordings of the relevant parameters were ever made. Much instrumentation, which was very limited at that time, would have been necessary, an appropriate aircraft allocated and many hours of flight testing expended. Such a thorough investigation was not possible but something had to be done – and quickly; although it is unlikely that these very brief losses of power had caused or contributed to damage to aircraft or pilots, it was necessary to do what we could to solve the problem, either by reducing the duration of the hesitation/cut or, preferably to eliminate both. All pilots deserved to enjoy maximum confidence in their aircraft.

The Solutions

Although this problem was known to Rolls-Royce before the war, it was not regarded as a serious impediment to operational performance, but following reports from Battle of Britain combat pilots, Rolls-Royce developed an anti-negative g carburettor. It was not, however, successful and was abandoned.

The Carburettor Section in RAE's Engine Department, headed by Miss Shilling, was asked to seek a solution. Since the weak cut was the lesser problem, she concentrated on solving, or at least reducing the severity of the rich cut as soon as possible. Clearly the most desirable solution would have been to limit the excessive surge of fuel only when the floats lost control, but this could not have been done quickly since any internal modifications to the carburettors which could have affected their performance would have required design and development and manufacturing time, plus flow rig and flight testing, which would have occupied months.

Work was put in hand in conjunction with Rolls-Royce and SU, and early in 1941 an interim solution was proposed by Carburettor Section, tried, tested and manufactured, and fitted to all relevant AVT/40 series carburettors which were subject to hesitations and cuts.

This required no modification of the carburettor itself; it was a simple brass restrictor in the form of a cup (figure 1), and later a flat disc (figure 2), fitted between the nipple on the carburettor end of the fuel inlet pipe and the union in the end of the fuel inlet gallery on the carburettor. The hole in the restrictor was sharp-edged and was large enough to allow the passage of sufficient fuel for maximum power operation of the engine, but prevented the subsequent deluge which followed without it. These restrictors, which were retro-fitted at service squadron airfields, were supplied with various orifice diameters in accordance with the maximum boost of the engines to which they were fitted.

The final solution, which required internal modifications to the carburettor was effective and cured both the weak and rich cuts. These modifications are shown in figure 3; it will be seen that the principal changes are the addition of twin shroud tubes around the main jet needle housings – of which there is one in each float chamber, and the replacement of the standard float needles with new ones which embody stems at their lower ends on which there are small discs, or pintles, the diameter of which is slightly smaller than that of the fuel inlet holes above them. See also Figure 3.

The two other changes, also shown in the diagrams, are the provision of a ball valve in the roof of each chamber to prevent fuel from entering the air vents under negative g conditions, and adjusters to allow setting of the pintle heights above the above-mentioned inlet holes, thus controlling the volume of fuel flowing through them into the chambers.

Instead of the fuel being drawn into the jet wells directly from holes in the float chamber floors as previously, these holes are now partly sealed off by the plates at the bottom of the shroud tubes which now provide an indirect, but the only, access from the chambers to the jet wells. Under 1 g (level flight) the tops of the tubes are beneath the fuel surface but, under negative g, when the main volume of fuel rises to the upper half of the chamber, the tube tops remain submerged by its lower level so that fuel, but not air, continues to pass down the tubes to the jet wells.

But, of course, if the negative gravity condition continues, the depth of fuel immediately above the tube will be quickly exhausted and, again, air will be drawn in. Unless, that is, more fuel is drawn in. This still happens but whereas previously the flow was unrestricted when the floats were fully down, in that position the flow is now limited by the size of the annulus formed between the pintle disc and the edge of the hole above it. And since the diameters of both are fixed, this size is dependent only on the height difference between the two. This is what the adjuster, which bears on the float mechanism, controls, and which is set to again restrict the flow to the maximum demanded by the engine at full combat power.

When positive g is restored, the floats rise, pushing the needles down to their seatings and again controlling the inlet fuel flow. The pintles drop with them and no longer restrict the flow, their function being limited to the negative g condition only.

Although these modifications were successful, they did indeed take a long time to install on Service aircraft, since every carburettor had to be removed from the engine and dismantled before the new parts could be fitted, after which they had to be flow tested and calibrated on purpose-built rigs prior to re-assembly and refitting to engines. This took many hours and was in contrast to the installation of the restrictor which could be completed in minutes. There was no way of measuring the effect of these changes on combat performance, but the restoration of pilot confidence when the chips were down was ample reward.

[Author's note: The words of former Hurricane pilot, Air Commodore Peter Brothers, D.F.C, D.S.O., probably sum up the opinion of pilots of Fighter Command:

"There is little more that I can say other than to express the relief we felt when Beatrice Shilling overcame the problem. How she did it I cannot recall, but believe it was quite a minor carburettor modification."]

FIGURE I

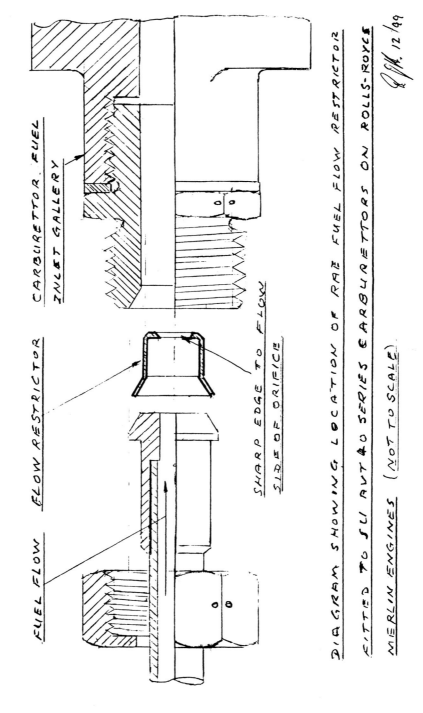

Figure 1. The original form of the anti-negative gravity fuel flow restrictor. Drawing supplied by RJ Newton

FIGURE 2

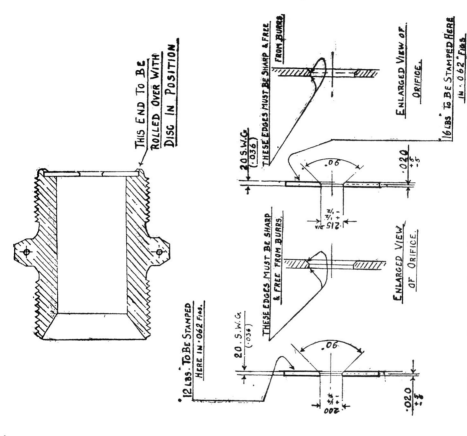

THIS END TO BE ROLLED OVER WITH DISC IN POSITION

12 LBS. TO BE STAMPED HERE IN ·062 FIGS.

20 S.W.G. (·036)

THESE EDGES MUST BE SHARP & FREE FROM BURRS.

·200 $+ \frac{3}{4}$ / $- \frac{1}{2}$

·020 $+ \frac{6}{5}$

·06

ENLARGED VIEW OF ORIFICE.

20 S.W.G. (·036)

THESE EDGES MUST BE SHARP & FREE FROM BURRS.

·215 $+ \frac{1}{2}$ / $- \frac{1}{2}$

·020 $+ \frac{6}{5}$

·06

ENLARGED VIEW OF ORIFICE.

16 LBS. TO BE STAMPED HERE IN ·062" FIGS.

Figure 2. The restrictor as shown later on Ministry of Air
Production modification orders. Public Record Office, London

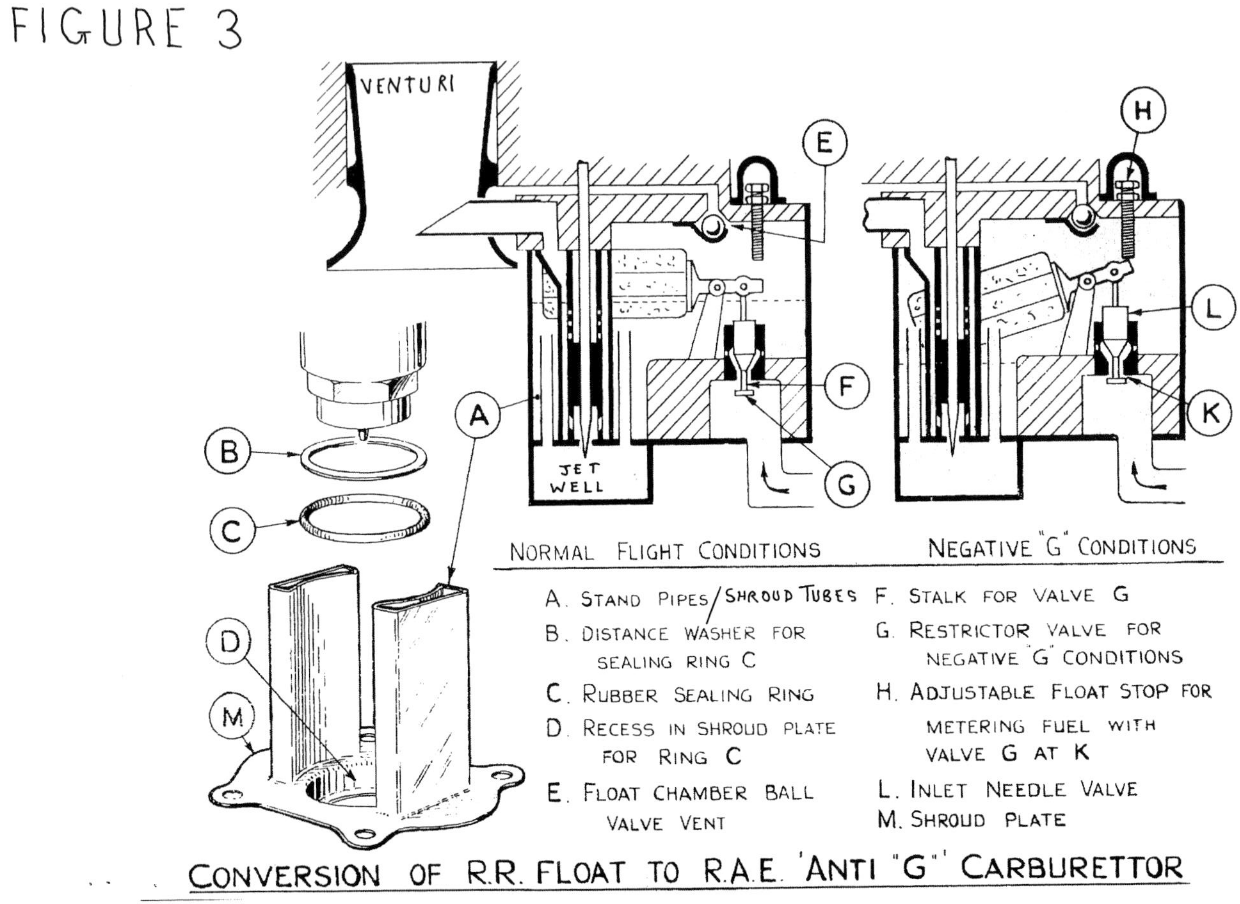

FIGURE 3

VENTURI

JET WELL

NORMAL FLIGHT CONDITIONS

NEGATIVE "G" CONDITIONS

A. STAND PIPES/SHROUD TUBES
B. DISTANCE WASHER FOR SEALING RING C
C. RUBBER SEALING RING
D. RECESS IN SHROUD PLATE FOR RING C
E. FLOAT CHAMBER BALL VALVE VENT

F. STALK FOR VALVE G
G. RESTRICTOR VALVE FOR NEGATIVE 'G' CONDITIONS
H. ADJUSTABLE FLOAT STOP FOR METERING FUEL WITH VALVE G AT K
L. INLET NEEDLE VALVE
M. SHROUD PLATE

CONVERSION OF R.R. FLOAT TO R.A.E. 'ANTI "G"' CARBURETTOR

Figure 3. The modifications to the SU AVT/40 carburettor that fully eliminated fuel cuts caused by negative gravity.

Appendix 11

Reports, technical notes and handbooks written by Beatrice Shilling. Based on the list of reports and notes appended to a C.V. written by her for the RAE before she retired.

Pegasus II M3 Air Publication, No. 1451C. 2nd Edition Revised 1937, Handbook.

Note No. E 3579. Note on diaphragm material for fuel pumps and pressure regulators. October 1937

Note No. E 3587. Note on the RAE Carburettor. (In collaboration with W.C.Clothier.) October 1937

Note No. E 3738. Note on engine throttle torque experiments. (In collaboration with K.C.Peggs.) October 1939

Note No. E 3798. Note on the RAE carburettor on a Hercules engine. (In collaboration with D. Ramsey.) June 1939

Note No. E 3901. Note on engine throttle torque and pressure drop experiments. (In collaboration with K.C.Peggs.) October 1939

Note No. E 3799. Note on the variation of the fuel flow delivered by a carburettor with changes in air temperature. Jan 1940

Report No. E 3800. Measurement of the air consumption of a poppet and a sleeve valve air-cooled radial aircraft engine with varying exhaust back pressure and intake temperature. Jan 1940

Progress Statement – Cutting out of Merlin engines under high acceleration. June 1940

Note No. E 3852. Further tests of the RAE carburettor. November 1940

Report No. E 3906. Fuel metering systems for engines operating at high altitudes. November 1941

Note No. E 3911. Note on the Bendix Stromberg venturi-injection carburettor. November 1941

Technical Note No. NG 26. Production timing of carburettors for British engines. August 1942

Technical Note No. ME 158. Preliminary assessment of a proposal for generating oxygen and nitrogen in an airborne unit for crew breathing and fuel tank purging. August 1953

Report M.E. No. 20. Report of Working Party on the internal cooling of high speed aircraft. July 1956. Published as "Internal Cooling of High Speed Aircraft" – *Journal of Refrigeration* 1956 (Received the Lightfoot Medal for the best paper read during the session 1956/57)

Accident Note No. Structures 306 Victor "b" MK2 Accident Investigation. Effect of Aircraft acceleration on Sunstrand constant speed main alternator drives. January 1960

Dept. Memorandum No. ME 264. Note on the possible forces acting in a test tank containing liquid oxygen following failure. December 1960

Internal Memorandum Memorandum on the pay of the Scientific Civil Service No. M.E. 252 and the working conditions of the Scientist in this Establishment. April 1962

Departmental Memo No. ME 311. Some notes on the possibilities of increasing the friction available between aircraft tyres and runways. March 1963

Report No. Mech. Eng. 26 Report of the M.O.A. Working Party on Auxiliary Power in Supersonic Aircraft. (Part author and editor as Chairman of the Working Party.) July, 1964

M.E. 1019 Aeronautical Research Council: Civil Aircraft Research Committee. "Some thoughts on "Reliability" Work." October 1965

Address on "Quality and Reliability of the Housewife." (Actually entitled "The Housewife and the Engineer"), to the Nottingham Branch of the Institution of Mechanical Engineers. October 1966.

Aeronautical Research Council; paper to Conference on "Friction and Wear in Tyres". February 1968

Paper to NASA Conference on RAE Work on tyres. November 1968

Article in "Design Engineering" : "The Design of a Bobsleigh" (With A. J. Rivers and E. S. Hiller.). November 1968

Bibliography

Barnes, C.H., *Bristol Aircraft since 1910.* Putnam, London, 1964.

Bingham, Victor. *Major Piston Aero Engines of World War II.* Airlife Publishing, Shrewsbury, 1998.

Birch, David. *Rolls-Royce and the Mustang Rolls-Royce.* Heritage Trust, Derby, 1997.

Bridgman, Leonard (compiled and edited). *Jane's All the Worlds Aircraft.* Sampson, Low, Marston and Company Ltd., London, Various years.

Brown, Don. *Miles Aircraft since 1925.* Putnam, London, 1970.

Brown, Capt. Eric, CBE, DSC, AFC, RN. *Wings of the Luftwaffe.* Airlife Publishing, Shrewsbury, 1993.

Cooper, Peter J. *Forever Farnborough.* Hikoki Publications, Aldershot, 1996.

Doe, Wing Commander Bob, DSO, DFC and Bar. *Fighter Pilot.* CCB Associates, Surrey, 1999.

Garbett, Mike and Goulding, Brian. *Lancaster.* Grange Books, Rochester, 1984.

Gunston, Bill, Fedden. *The Life of Roy Feddon.* Rolls-Royce Heritage Trust, Derby, 1998.

Gunston, Bill. *Rolls-Royce Aero Engines.* PLS, 1989.

Harvey-Bailey, Alec. *The Merlin in Perspective – the combat years.* Rolls-Royce Heritage Trust, Derby, 1983.

Henshaw, Alec. *Sigh for a Merlin.* Air Data Publications, 1996.

Heron, S.D., *A History of the Aircraft Piston Engine.* Ethyl Corporation (Research and Development Department), Detroit USA, 1961.

Hobson (Aircraft and Motor) Components Ltd., *The Hobson RAE Master Control Injector* (Handbook)1952.

Jenkins, Alan. *The Twenties.* William Heinemann, London, 1974.

Middlebrook, Martin and Chris Everitt. *The Bomber Command War Diaries.* Midland Publishing, Leicester, 2000.

Morgan, E. B. and E. Shacklady. *Spitfire, the History.* Key Publishing, 1989.

Overy, Richard. *Bomber Command 1939 – 1945.* Harper Collins, London, 1997.

Price, Alfred. *Spitfire.* Grange Books, PLC, Rochester 1999.

Priestley, J. B., *The Edwardians.* Heinemann, London, 1970.

Rubbra, A. A., *Rolls-Royce Piston Engines – A Designer Remembers.* Rolls-Royce Heritage Trust, Derby, 1990.

Sturtivant, Ray. *The Swordfish Story.* Cassel & Co, London 1993.

Turnill, Reginald and Arthur Reed. *Farnborough, the Story of the RAE.* Robert Hale, London,1980.

Schlaifer, Robert. *Development of Aircraft Engines.* Soldiers Field Boston, USA, 1949.

Wood, Derek. *Project Cancelled.* Tri-Service Press, 1976.

Index